TRIG IDENTITIES

Practice Workbook with Answers

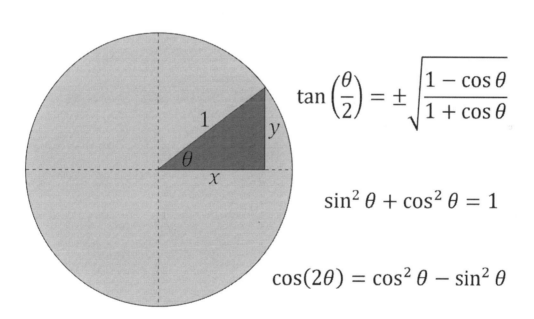

$$\tan\left(\frac{\theta}{2}\right) = \pm\sqrt{\frac{1-\cos\theta}{1+\cos\theta}}$$

$$\sin^2\theta + \cos^2\theta = 1$$

$$\cos(2\theta) = \cos^2\theta - \sin^2\theta$$

Chris McMullen, Ph.D.

Trig Identities Practice Workbook with Answers

Chris McMullen, Ph.D.

Zishka Publishing

ISBN: 978-1-941691-38-0

Mathematics > Trigonometry

Mathematics > Precalculus

Contents

Introduction

This workbook helps students understand a variety of standard trig identities. Each chapter begins with a concise introduction to pertinent concepts and includes fully solved examples to help serve as a guide. Hints and answers to the problems can be found at the back of the book. The following kinds of trig identities are covered:

- A Pythagorean identity follows from the Pythagorean theorem. For example, $\sin^2 x + \cos^2 x = 1$ can be derived by applying the Pythagorean theorem to a right triangle.
- An odd/even function identity refers to identities such as $\cos(-x) = \cos x$ or $\sin(-x) = -\sin x$. Each of the six standard trig functions (sine, cosine, tangent, secant, cosecant, and cotangent) is either an even function or an odd function.
- An angle sum identity involves the sum (or difference) of two angles in the argument of a trig function, like $\cos(x + y) = \cos x \cos y - \sin x \sin y$.
- In a double angle identity, the argument of one trig function has twice the angle of another trig function, such as $\cos(2x) = \cos^2 x - \sin^2 x$.
- In a half-angle identity, the argument of one trig function has one-half the angle of another trig function, such as $\cos\left(\frac{x}{2}\right) = \pm\sqrt{\frac{1+\cos x}{2}}$.
- In a multiple angle identity, the argument of one trig function is a multiple of the angle of another trig function, like $\cos(3x) = 4\cos^3 x - 3\cos x$.
- In a power reduction identity, a power of a trig function is expressed in terms of smaller powers of trig functions, like $\cos^2 x = \frac{1+\cos(2x)}{2}$.
- Sum/product identities relate the sum of two trig functions to the product of two trig functions, like $\cos x + \cos y = 2\cos\left(\frac{x+y}{2}\right)\cos\left(\frac{x-y}{2}\right)$.
- Angle shifting identities shift the angle, like $\cos\left(\frac{\pi}{2} - x\right) = \sin x$.
- The law of sines and law of cosines apply even to acute or obtuse triangles.
- An inverse function identity involves an inverse trig function, such as $\sin^{-1} x + \cos^{-1} x = \frac{\pi}{2}$.

1 Pythagorean Identities

Recall that the standard trig functions relate the sides of a right triangle. The longest side is the **hypotenuse**; it is opposite to the right angle. One leg is called the **opposite** side; it is opposite to the angle in the argument of the trig function. The other leg is called the **adjacent** side; the angle in the argument of the trig function is formed by the adjacent and the hypotenuse. The six standard trig functions are the cosine, sine, tangent, secant, cosecant, and cotangent.

$$\cos x = \frac{\text{adj.}}{\text{hyp.}} \quad , \quad \sin x = \frac{\text{opp.}}{\text{hyp.}} \quad , \quad \tan x = \frac{\text{opp.}}{\text{adj.}}$$

$$\sec x = \frac{\text{hyp.}}{\text{adj.}} \quad , \quad \csc x = \frac{\text{hyp.}}{\text{opp.}} \quad , \quad \cot x = \frac{\text{adj.}}{\text{opp.}}$$

Note that secant and cosine are reciprocals, sine and cosecant are reciprocals, and tangent and cotangent are reciprocals. (Although some students intuitively expect the cosecant and cosine to go together because they both have co's in their names, these two functions are not reciprocals. The cosecant function is the reciprocal of the sine function, whereas the secant function is the reciprocal of the cosine function.)

$$\sec x = \frac{1}{\cos x} \quad , \quad \csc x = \frac{1}{\sin x} \quad , \quad \cot x = \frac{1}{\tan x}$$

Also note that tangent and cotangent can be expressed as the following quotients:

$$\tan x = \frac{\sin x}{\cos x} \quad , \quad \cot x = \frac{\cos x}{\sin x}$$

According to the **Pythagorean theorem**, which applies to every right triangle, the square of the adjacent side plus the square of the opposite side equals the square of the hypotenuse. For example, for the right triangle shown below, the hypotenuse is c, the side opposite to x is b, and the side adjacent to x is a. The Pythagorean theorem for this right triangle is:

$$a^2 + b^2 = c^2$$

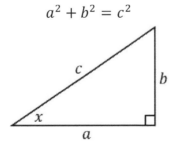

The definitions of the standard trig functions can be combined with the Pythagorean theorem to form the following **Pythagorean identities**. We will derive the identity on the left in Example 1; the others will be explored in the exercises.

$$\sin^2 x + \cos^2 x = 1 \quad , \quad \tan^2 x + 1 = \sec^2 x \quad , \quad 1 + \cot^2 x = \csc^2 x$$

The above identities (along with the reciprocal identities for secant, cosecant, and cotangent from the previous page) allow any trig function to be expressed exclusively in terms of any other trig function. For example, we can express the tangent function in terms of the cosine function as $\tan x = \pm \frac{\sqrt{1-\cos^2 x}}{\cos x}$ (see Example 2). We will explore other trig identities of this nature in the exercises.

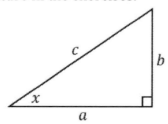

Example 1. Derive $\sin^2 x + \cos^2 x = 1$.

Solution. Consider the right triangle shown above. The Pythagorean theorem is:

$$a^2 + b^2 = c^2$$

Divide both sides of the equation by c^2.

$$\left(\frac{a}{c}\right)^2 + \left(\frac{b}{c}\right)^2 = 1$$

For angle x above, the adjacent is a, the opposite is b, and the hypotenuse is c. Therefore, $\cos x = \frac{a}{c}$ and $\sin x = \frac{b}{c}$. Substitute these expressions into the previous equation.

$$\sin^2 x + \cos^2 x = 1$$

Note: Alternatively, if you draw a right triangle for the unit circle, the hypotenuse will be 1 and you can derive the above identity in fewer steps.

Example 2. Show that $\tan x = \pm \frac{\sqrt{1-\cos^2 x}}{\cos x}$.

Solution. Solve for sine in the Pythagorean identity. When you take the square root, consider both possible signs. For example, $\sqrt{9} = \pm 3$ because $(-3)^2 = 9$ and $3^2 = 9$.

$$\sin x = \pm\sqrt{1 - \cos^2 x}$$

Substitute this expression into the ratio formula for tangent (from the previous page):

$$\tan x = \frac{\sin x}{\cos x} = \pm \frac{\sqrt{1 - \cos^2 x}}{\cos x}$$

Chapter 1 Exercises

1. Derive $\tan^2 x + 1 = \sec^2 x$.

2. Derive $1 + \cot^2 x = \csc^2 x$.

3. Show that $\sin x = \pm\sqrt{1 - \cos^2 x}$.

4. Show that $\sec x = \pm\sqrt{1 + \tan^2 x}$.

5. Show that $\tan x = \pm\dfrac{\sin x}{\sqrt{1-\sin^2 x}}$.

6. Show that $\sin x = \pm\dfrac{\sqrt{\sec^2 x-1}}{\sec x}$.

7. Show that $\csc x = \pm \frac{\sqrt{1+\tan^2 x}}{\tan x}$.

8. Show that $\tan x = \pm \frac{1}{\sqrt{\csc^2 x - 1}}$.

9. Given that $\sin x = 0.6$, determine $\cos x$ without taking an inverse.

10. Given that $\cos x = \frac{5}{13}$, determine $\tan x$ without taking an inverse.

11. Given that $\tan x = \frac{\sqrt{5}}{2}$, determine $\cos x$ without taking an inverse.

12. Given that $\sec x = \frac{8}{7}$, determine $\cot x$ without taking an inverse.

13. Solve for x in the following equation (assuming that $0 \le x \le 2\pi$):
$$5 \sin^2 x - 3 \cos^2 x = 1$$

14. Solve for x in the following equation (assuming that $0 \le x \le 2\pi$):
$$\sin^2 x \tan^2 x = 3 - \sin^2 x$$

15. Solve for x in the following equation (assuming that $0 \le x \le 2\pi$):

$$\sin x - \sqrt{3}\cos^2 x = \frac{\sqrt{3}}{4}$$

16. Solve for x in the following equation (assuming that $0 \le x \le 2\pi$):

$$\sqrt{3} + \tan x = 2 + \sec x$$

2 Odd and Even Functions

We use the notation $f(x)$ to mean that f is a **function** of x. It is important to realize that $f(x)$ does **not** mean to multiply f by x. For example, sine is a function. When we write $y(x) = \sin(x)$, we are indicating that y is a function of x.

A function is considered to be **even** if changing the sign of the argument leaves the value of the function unchanged. For example, $y = x^2$ is an even function because $y(-x) = y(x)$. To see this with numbers, let $x = \pm 3$, for which $y(-3) = (-3)^2 = 9$ is the same as $y(3) = (3)^2 = 9$. If $y(-x) = y(x)$ for all possible x for which the function is defined, the function is even.

A function is considered to be **odd** if changing the sign of the argument changes the sign of the value of the function. For example, $y = x^3$ is an odd function because $y(-x) = -y(x)$. To see this with numbers, let $x = \pm 2$, for which $y(-2) = (-2)^3 = -8$ is the negative of $y(2) = (2)^3 = 8$. If $y(-x) = -y(x)$ for all possible x for which the function is defined, the function is odd.

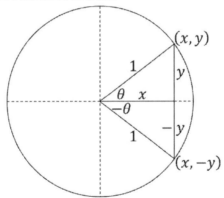

Example 1. Show that the sine function is an odd function.

Solution. One way to do this is to consider a right triangle on the unit circle (as shown above). The point (x, y) lies at one vertex of the triangle and also lies on the circle. The angle θ is measured counterclockwise from the $+x$-axis. The adjacent to θ is x, the opposite to θ is y, and the hypotenuse is 1 because it is a radius of the unit circle. Since the sine function equals the opposite over the hypotenuse,

$$\sin \theta = \frac{y}{1} = y$$

If we change the sign of θ, the point will have coordinates $(x, -y)$, as shown on the previous page. The opposite will be $-y$ and the hypotenuse will still be 1:

$$\sin(-\theta) = \frac{-y}{1} = -y = -\sin\theta$$

An alternative method is to graph the sine function. This graph is antisymmetric about the vertical axis, such that for any point (x, y) on the curve, there is an antisymmetric point on the curve with the opposite sign of both x and y. For example, when $x = \frac{\pi}{3}$, the sine function is $\sin\left(\frac{\pi}{3}\right) = \frac{\sqrt{3}}{2}$, and when $x = -\frac{\pi}{3}$, the sine function is $\sin\left(-\frac{\pi}{3}\right) = -\frac{\sqrt{3}}{2}$, showing that $\sin\left(\frac{\pi}{3}\right) = -\sin\left(-\frac{\pi}{3}\right)$.

Example 2. Show that the cosine function is an even function.
Solution. One way to do this is to consider a right triangle on the unit circle (as shown on the previous page). The point (x, y) lies at one vertex of the triangle and also lies on the circle. The angle θ is measured counterclockwise from the $+x$-axis. The adjacent to θ is x, the opposite to θ is y, and the hypotenuse is 1 because it is a radius of the unit circle. Since the cosine function equals the adjacent over the hypotenuse,

$$\cos\theta = \frac{x}{1} = x$$

If we change the sign of θ, the point will have coordinates $(x, -y)$, as shown on the previous page. The adjacent will still be x and the hypotenuse will still be 1:

$$\cos(-\theta) = \frac{x}{1} = x = \cos\theta$$

An alternative method is to graph the cosine function. This graph is symmetric about the vertical axis, such that for any point (x, y) on the curve, there is a symmetric point on the curve with the opposite sign of x and the same value of y. For example, when $x = \frac{\pi}{3}$, the cosine function is $\cos\left(\frac{\pi}{3}\right) = \frac{1}{2}$, and when $x = -\frac{\pi}{3}$, the cosine function is $\cos\left(-\frac{\pi}{3}\right) = \frac{1}{2}$, showing that $\cos\left(-\frac{\pi}{3}\right) = \cos\left(\frac{\pi}{3}\right)$.

Chapter 2 Exercises

1. Show that the tangent function is an odd function.

2. Show that the secant function is an even function.

3. Show that the cosecant function is an odd function.

4. Show that the cotangent function is an odd function.

5. Show that $\sin^2 \theta$ is an even function.

6. Show that $\cos^2 \theta$ is an even function.

7. Show that $\sin^3 \theta$ is an odd function.

8. Show that $\cos^3 \theta$ is an even function.

9. Show that $\sin\theta\cos\theta$ is an odd function.

10. Show that $\csc\theta\cot\theta$ is an even function.

11. Given that $\sin x = 0.15$, determine $\sin(-x)$ without taking an inverse.

12. Given that $\cos x = \frac{3}{4}$, determine $\cos(-x)$ without taking an inverse.

13. Given that $\tan x = 0.7$, determine $\tan(-x)$ without taking an inverse.

14. Given that $\cot x = \frac{3}{2}$, determine $\cot(-x)$ without taking an inverse.

15. Given that $\sec x = 1.6$, determine $\sec(-x)$ without taking an inverse.

16. Given that $\csc x = -\frac{5}{4}$, determine $\csc(-x)$ without taking an inverse.

3 Angle Sum Formulas

The basic sum of angles formulas are:
$$\cos(x + y) = \cos x \cos y - \sin x \sin y$$
$$\sin(x + y) = \sin x \cos y + \sin y \cos x$$
$$\tan(x + y) = \frac{\tan x + \tan y}{1 - \tan x \tan y}$$
$$\sec(x + y) = \frac{\sec x \sec y \csc x \csc y}{\csc x \csc y - \sec x \sec y}$$
$$\csc(x + y) = \frac{\sec x \sec y \csc x \csc y}{\sec x \csc y + \csc x \sec y}$$
$$\cot(x + y) = \frac{\cot x \cot y - 1}{\cot y + \cot x}$$

The basic difference of angles formulas are:
$$\cos(x - y) = \cos x \cos y + \sin x \sin y$$
$$\sin(x - y) = \sin x \cos y - \sin y \cos x$$
$$\tan(x - y) = \frac{\tan x - \tan y}{1 + \tan x \tan y}$$
$$\sec(x - y) = \frac{\sec x \sec y \csc x \csc y}{\csc x \csc y + \sec x \sec y}$$
$$\csc(x - y) = \frac{\sec x \sec y \csc x \csc y}{\sec x \csc y - \csc x \sec y}$$
$$\cot(x - y) = \frac{\cot x \cot y + 1}{\cot y - \cot x}$$

The two sets of formulas are often combined together with $\pm$ notation:
$$\cos(x \pm y) = \cos x \cos y \mp \sin x \sin y$$
$$\sin(x \pm y) = \sin x \cos y \pm \sin y \cos x$$
$$\tan(x \pm y) = \frac{\tan x \pm \tan y}{1 \mp \tan x \tan y}$$
$$\sec(x \pm y) = \frac{\sec x \sec y \csc x \csc y}{\csc x \csc y \mp \sec x \sec y}$$
$$\csc(x \pm y) = \frac{\sec x \sec y \csc x \csc y}{\sec x \csc y \pm \csc x \sec y}$$
$$\cot(x \pm y) = \frac{\cot x \cot y \mp 1}{\cot y \pm \cot x}$$

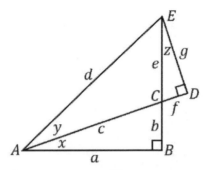

Example 1. Derive $\cos(x \pm y) = \cos x \cos y \mp \sin x \sin y$.

Solution. In $\triangle ABE$ in the diagram above, the adjacent of $x + y$ is a and the hypotenuse is d:

$$\cos(x + y) = \frac{a}{d}$$

In $\triangle ABC$, the adjacent of x is a, the opposite of x is b, and the hypotenuse is c:

$$\cos x = \frac{a}{c} \quad , \quad \sin x = \frac{b}{c}$$

In $\triangle ADE$, the adjacent of y is $c + f$, the opposite of y is g, and the hypotenuse is d:

$$\cos y = \frac{c + f}{d} \quad , \quad \sin y = \frac{g}{d}$$

In $\triangle CDE$, the adjacent of z is g, the opposite of z is f, and the hypotenuse is e:

$$\cos z = \frac{g}{e} \quad , \quad \sin z = \frac{f}{e}$$

Since $\angle ACB \cong \angle DCE$ (because they are vertical angles), it follows that $z = x$ (because the three angles in $\triangle ABC$ and $\triangle CDE$ must each add up to π rad). Thus, we may rewrite the above equations with x in place of z.

$$\cos x = \frac{g}{e} \quad , \quad \sin x = \frac{f}{e}$$

Since $\cos x = \frac{a}{c}$ and $\cos x = \frac{g}{e}$, it follows that $\frac{a}{c} = \frac{g}{e}$. Since $\sin x = \frac{b}{c}$ and $\sin x = \frac{f}{e}$, it also follows that $\frac{b}{c} = \frac{f}{e}$. If we isolate g and f in these equations, we get:

$$g = \frac{ae}{c} \quad , \quad f = \frac{be}{c}$$

Plug these expressions into the equations for y.

$$\cos y = \frac{c + f}{d} = \frac{c}{d} + \frac{be}{cd} \quad , \quad \sin y = \frac{g}{d} = \frac{ae}{cd}$$

Plug $\cos x = \frac{a}{c}$, $\sin x = \frac{b}{c}$, $\cos y = \frac{c}{d} + \frac{be}{cd}$, and $\sin y = \frac{ae}{cd}$ into $\cos x \cos y - \sin x \sin y$.

$$\cos x \cos y - \sin x \sin y = \frac{a}{c}\left(\frac{c}{d} + \frac{be}{cd}\right) - \frac{b}{c}\frac{ae}{cd} = \frac{ac}{cd} + \frac{abe}{c^2 d} - \frac{abe}{c^2 d} = \frac{ac}{cd} = \frac{a}{d}$$

Since our first equation was $\cos(x+y) = \frac{a}{d}$, we have now shown that

$$\cos(x+y) = \cos x \cos y - \sin x \sin y$$

To complete the solution, we also need to work out $\cos(x-y)$. To do this, we will replace y with $-y$ in the equation above and apply the formulas $\cos(-\theta) = \cos\theta$ and $\sin(-\theta) = -\sin\theta$ from Chapter 2.

$$\cos(x-y) = \cos x \cos(-y) - \sin x \sin(-y)$$
$$\cos(x-y) = \cos x \cos y - \sin x \,(-\sin y)$$
$$\cos(x-y) = \cos x \cos y + \sin x \sin y$$

Combine the equation $\cos(x+y) = \cos x \cos y - \sin x \sin y$ together with the equation $\cos(x-y) = \cos x \cos y + \sin x \sin y$ to get the final answer:

$$\cos(x \pm y) = \cos x \cos y \mp \sin x \sin y$$

Note: The $\mp$ sign means that the $-$ sign is used for $\cos(x+y)$ and the $+$ sign is used for $\cos(x-y)$. That is, $\mp$ uses opposite signs compared to $\pm$.

Example 2. Derive $\tan(x \pm y) = \frac{\tan x \pm \tan y}{1 \mp \tan x \tan y}$.

Solution. Begin by expressing $\tan(x \pm y)$ in terms of sine and cosine.

$$\tan(x \pm y) = \frac{\sin(x \pm y)}{\cos(x \pm y)}$$

Now apply the sum (or difference) of angle formulas for sine and cosine.

$$\tan(x \pm y) = \frac{\sin x \cos y \pm \sin y \cos x}{\cos x \cos y \mp \sin x \sin y}$$

Divide the numerator and denominator each by $\cos x \cos y$. Note that $\frac{\cos y}{\cos y} = 1$ and $\frac{\cos x}{\cos x} = 1$.

$$\tan(x \pm y) = \frac{\dfrac{\sin x \cos y}{\cos x \cos y} \pm \dfrac{\sin y \cos x}{\cos x \cos y}}{1 \mp \dfrac{\sin x \sin y}{\cos x \cos y}} = \frac{\tan x \pm \tan y}{1 \mp \tan x \tan y}$$

Chapter 3 Exercises

1. Derive $\sin(x \pm y) = \sin x \cos y \pm \sin y \cos x$.

2. Derive $\sec(x \pm y) = \dfrac{\sec x \sec y \csc x \csc y}{\csc x \csc y \mp \sec x \sec y}$.

3. Derive $\csc(x \pm y) = \dfrac{\sec x \sec y \csc x \csc y}{\sec x \csc y \pm \csc x \sec y}$.

4. Derive $\cot(x \pm y) = \dfrac{\cot x \cot y \mp 1}{\cot y \pm \cot x}$.

5. Use a sum or difference of angles formula to find sin 15°.

6. Use a sum or difference of angles formula to find cos 15°.

7. Use a sum or difference of angles formula to find tan 75°.

8. Use a sum or difference of angles formula to find sec 105°.

9. Use a sum or difference of angles formula to find csc 105°.

10. Use a sum or difference of angles formula to find cot 165°.

4 Double Angle Formulas

The standard double angle formulas are:
$$\sin(2x) = 2\sin x \cos x \quad , \quad \cos(2x) = \cos^2 x - \sin^2 x$$
$$\tan(2x) = \frac{2\tan x}{1 - \tan^2 x} \quad , \quad \cot(2x) = \frac{\cot^2 x - 1}{2\cot x}$$
$$\sec(2x) = \frac{\sec^2 x}{2 - \sec^2 x} \quad , \quad \csc(2x) = \frac{\sec x \csc x}{2}$$
$$\sin(2x) = \frac{2\tan x}{1 + \tan^2 x} \quad , \quad \cos(2x) = 2\cos^2 x - 1$$
$$\cos(2x) = 1 - 2\sin^2 x \quad , \quad \cos(2x) = \frac{1 - \tan^2 x}{1 + \tan^2 x}$$

Example 1. Derive $\cos(2x) = \cos^2 x - \sin^2 x$.

Solution. Set $y = x$ in the sum of angles formula (Chapter 3) for cosine.
$$\cos(x + x) = \cos x \cos x - \sin x \sin x = \cos^2 x - \sin^2 x$$

Example 2. Derive $\cos(2x) = 1 - 2\sin^2 x$.

Solution. Recall the Pythagorean identity $\sin^2 x + \cos^2 x = 1$ from Chapter 1. Rewrite this as $\cos^2 x = 1 - \sin^2 x$. Substitute this into the identity from Example 1.
$$\cos(2x) = \cos^2 x - \sin^2 x = 1 - \sin^2 x - \sin^2 x = 1 - 2\sin^2 x$$

Chapter 4 Exercises

1. Derive $\sin(2x) = 2\sin x \cos x$.

2. Derive $\tan(2x) = \frac{2\tan x}{1 - \tan^2 x}$.

3. Derive $\cot(2x) = \frac{\cot^2 x - 1}{2\cot x}$.

4. Derive $\cos(2x) = 2\cos^2 x - 1$.

5. Derive $\csc(2x) = \frac{\sec x \csc x}{2}$.

6. Derive $\sec(2x) = \frac{\sec^2 x}{2 - \sec^2 x}$.

7. Derive $\sin(2x) = \frac{2\tan x}{1 + \tan^2 x}$.

8. Derive $\cos(2x) = \frac{1 - \tan^2 x}{1 + \tan^2 x}$.

9. Solve for x in the following equation (assuming that $0 \le x \le 2\pi$):
$$12 \sin x \cos x = 3$$

10. Solve for x in the following equation (assuming that $0 \le x \le 2\pi$):
$$2 \cos^2 x + \cos(2x) = 1$$

11. Solve for x in the following equation (assuming that $0 \le x \le 2\pi$):
$$2\sqrt{3} \tan x = 1 - \tan^2 x$$

12. Solve for x in the following equation (assuming that $0 \le x \le 2\pi$):
$$2 \sin x \cos x = \sqrt{3} \cos^2 x - \sqrt{3} \sin^2 x$$

4 Double Angle Formulas

13. Solve for x in the following equation (assuming that $0 \le x \le 2\pi$):
$$4 \sin x = -\sqrt{3} \sec x$$

14. Solve for x in the following equation (assuming that $0 \le x \le 2\pi$):
$$4 \cos^2 x - 3 = 4 \cos(2x)$$

15. Solve for x in the following equation (assuming that $0 \le x \le 2\pi$):
$$\tan(2x) = -\sec(2x) \cos x$$

16. Solve for x in the following equation (assuming that $0 \le x \le 2\pi$):
$$\csc(2x) = -2 \cos(2x)$$

5 Half-Angle Formulas

The standard half-angle formulas are:

$$\sin^2\left(\frac{x}{2}\right) = \frac{1 - \cos x}{2} \quad , \quad \cos^2\left(\frac{x}{2}\right) = \frac{1 + \cos x}{2}$$

$$\tan^2\left(\frac{x}{2}\right) = \frac{1 - \cos x}{1 + \cos x} \quad , \quad \cot^2\left(\frac{x}{2}\right) = \frac{1 + \cos x}{1 - \cos x}$$

$$\tan\left(\frac{x}{2}\right) = \csc x - \cot x \quad , \quad \cot\left(\frac{x}{2}\right) = \csc x + \cot x$$

$$\tan\left(\frac{x}{2}\right) = \frac{\sin x}{1 + \cos x} \quad , \quad \cot\left(\frac{x}{2}\right) = \frac{\sin x}{1 - \cos x}$$

$$\tan\left(\frac{x}{2}\right) = \frac{1 - \cos x}{\sin x} \quad , \quad \cot\left(\frac{x}{2}\right) = \frac{1 + \cos x}{\sin x}$$

$$\tan\left(\frac{x}{2}\right) = \frac{\tan x}{1 + \sec x} \quad , \quad \cot\left(\frac{x}{2}\right) = \frac{1 + \sec x}{\tan x}$$

$$\tan\left(\frac{x}{2}\right) = \frac{-1 \pm \sqrt{1 + \tan^2 x}}{\tan x} \quad , \quad \cot\left(\frac{x}{2}\right) = \frac{\tan x}{-1 \pm \sqrt{1 + \tan^2 x}}$$

$$\sec^2\left(\frac{x}{2}\right) = \frac{2}{1 + \cos x} \quad , \quad \csc^2\left(\frac{x}{2}\right) = \frac{2}{1 - \cos x}$$

Example 1. Derive $\cos^2\left(\frac{x}{2}\right) = \frac{1 + \cos x}{2}$.

Solution. Begin with the following form of the double angle formula (Chapter 4) for cosine written in terms of y.

$$\cos(2y) = 2\cos^2 y - 1$$

Add 1 to both sides of the equation.

$$1 + \cos(2y) = 2\cos^2 y$$

Divide both sides of the equation by 2.

$$\frac{1 + \cos(2y)}{2} = \cos^2 y$$

Let $y = \frac{x}{2}$ such that $2y = x$.

$$\frac{1 + \cos x}{2} = \cos^2\left(\frac{x}{2}\right)$$

Example 2. Derive $\tan^2\left(\frac{x}{2}\right) = \frac{1-\cos x}{1+\cos x}$.

Solution. Write tangent as the ratio of sine to cosine, and then apply the half-angle formulas for sine and cosine.

$$\tan^2\left(\frac{x}{2}\right) = \frac{\sin^2\left(\frac{x}{2}\right)}{\cos^2\left(\frac{x}{2}\right)} = \frac{\dfrac{1-\cos x}{2}}{\dfrac{1+\cos x}{2}} = \frac{1-\cos x}{2}\frac{2}{1+\cos x} = \frac{1-\cos x}{1+\cos x}$$

Note that the 2's cancel. Recall that the way to divide two fractions is to multiply by the reciprocal of the second fraction.

Chapter 5 Exercises

1. Derive $\sin^2\left(\frac{x}{2}\right) = \frac{1-\cos x}{2}$.

2. Derive $\cot^2\left(\frac{x}{2}\right) = \frac{1+\cos x}{1-\cos x}$.

3. Derive $\tan\left(\frac{x}{2}\right) = \frac{\sin x}{1+\cos x}$.

4. Derive $\tan\left(\frac{x}{2}\right) = \frac{1-\cos x}{\sin x}$.

5. Derive $\tan\left(\frac{x}{2}\right) = \csc x - \cot x$.

6. Derive $\cot\left(\frac{x}{2}\right) = \csc x + \cot x$.

7. Derive $\cot\left(\frac{x}{2}\right) = \frac{1+\sec x}{\tan x}$.

8. Derive $\tan\left(\frac{x}{2}\right) = \frac{-1\pm\sqrt{1+\tan^2 x}}{\tan x}$.

9. Derive $\sec^2\left(\frac{x}{2}\right) = \frac{2}{1+\cos x}$.

10. Derive $\csc^2\left(\frac{x}{2}\right) = \frac{2}{1-\cos x}$.

11. Use a half-angle formula to find $\sin 15°$.

12. Use a half-angle formula to find $\cos 15°$.

13. Use a half-angle formula to find $\tan 75°$.

14. Use a half-angle formula to find $\cos 105°$.

15. Use a half-angle formula to find sin 165°.

16. Use a half-angle formula to find sec 67.5°.

17. Use a half-angle formula to find csc 112.5°.

18. Use a half-angle formula to find cot 157.5°.

19. Use a half-angle formula to find sin 7.5°.

20. Use a half-angle formula to find cos 11.25°.

6 Triple Angle Formulas

The standard triple angle formulas are:
$$\sin(3x) = 3\sin x - 4\sin^3 x \quad , \quad \cos(3x) = 4\cos^3 x - 3\cos x$$
$$\tan(3x) = \frac{3\tan x - \tan^3 x}{1 - 3\tan^2 x} \quad , \quad \cot(3x) = \frac{3\cot x - \cot^3 x}{1 - 3\cot^2 x}$$
$$\sec(3x) = \frac{\sec^3 x}{4 - 3\sec^2 x} \quad , \quad \csc(3x) = \frac{\csc^3 x}{3\csc^2 x - 4}$$

Example 1. Derive $\cos(3x) = 4\cos^3 x - 3\cos x$.

Solution. Set $y = 2x$ in the sum of angles formula (Chapter 3) for cosine.
$$\cos(x + 2x) = \cos x \cos(2x) - \sin x \sin(2x)$$
Apply the double angle formulas (Chapter 4) for cosine and sine.
$$\cos(3x) = \cos x \left(\cos^2 x - \sin^2 x\right) - \sin x \left(2\sin x \cos x\right)$$
Distribute.
$$\cos(3x) = \cos^3 x - \sin^2 x \cos x - 2\sin^2 x \cos x$$
Combine like terms.
$$\cos(3x) = \cos^3 x - 3\sin^2 x \cos x$$
Recall the Pythagorean identity $\sin^2 x + \cos^2 x = 1$ from Chapter 1. Rewrite this as $\sin^2 x = 1 - \cos^2 x$. Substitute this into the previous equation.
$$\cos(3x) = \cos^3 x - 3(1 - \cos^2 x)\cos x$$
Distribute. Note that $-3(1 - \cos^2 x)\cos x = -3\cos x + 3\cos^3 x$. (When the minus sign is distributed, the two minus signs make the last term positive.)
$$\cos(3x) = \cos^3 x - 3\cos x + 3\cos^3 x$$
Combine like terms.
$$\cos(3x) = 4\cos^3 x - 3\cos x$$

Chapter 6 Exercises

1. Derive $\sin(3x) = 3\sin x - 4\sin^3 x$.

2. Derive $\tan(3x) = \dfrac{3\tan x - \tan^3 x}{1 - 3\tan^2 x}$.

3. Derive $\cot(3x) = \frac{3\cot x - \cot^3 x}{1 - 3\cot^2 x}$.

4. Derive $\sec(3x) = \frac{\sec^3 x}{4 - 3\sec^2 x}$.

5. Derive $\csc(3x) = \dfrac{\csc^3 x}{3\csc^2 x - 4}$.

7 Power Reduction Formulas

Power reduction formulas express a power of a trig function in terms of trig functions with lower powers.

The first four power reduction formulas for sine and cosine are:

$$\sin^2 x = \frac{1 - \cos(2x)}{2} \quad , \quad \cos^2 x = \frac{1 + \cos(2x)}{2}$$

$$\sin^3 x = \frac{3 \sin x - \sin(3x)}{4} \quad , \quad \cos^3 x = \frac{3 \cos x + \cos(3x)}{4}$$

$$\sin^4 x = \frac{3 - 4 \cos(2x) + \cos(4x)}{8} \quad , \quad \cos^4 x = \frac{3 + 4 \cos(2x) + \cos(4x)}{8}$$

$$\sin^5 x = \frac{10 \sin x - 5 \sin(3x) + \sin(5x)}{16} \quad , \quad \cos^5 x = \frac{10 \cos x + 5 \cos(3x) + \cos(5x)}{16}$$

The first two power reduction formulas for tangent and cotangent are:

$$\tan^2 x = 1 - 2 \frac{\tan x}{\tan(2x)} \quad , \quad \cot^2 x = 2 \cot(2x) \cot x + 1$$

$$\tan^3 x = 3 \tan x + 2 \tan(3x) - 6 \frac{\tan x \tan(3x)}{\tan(2x)}$$

$$\cot^3 x = 3 \cot x + 2 \cot(3x) + 6 \cot x \cot(2x) \cot(3x)$$

The first two power reduction formulas for secant and cosecant are:

$$\sec^2 x = \frac{2 \sec(2x)}{\sec(2x) + 1} \quad , \quad \csc^2 x = \frac{2 \sec(2x)}{\sec(2x) - 1}$$

$$\sec^3 x = 4 \sec(3x) - 6 \frac{\sec(2x) \sec(3x)}{\sec(2x) + 1}$$

$$\csc^3 x = -4 \csc(3x) + 6 \frac{\sec(2x) \csc(3x)}{\sec(2x) - 1}$$

Example 1. Derive $\cos^2 x = \frac{1 + \cos(2x)}{2}$.

Solution. Begin with one of the double angle formulas (Chapter 4) for cosine.

$$\cos(2x) = 2 \cos^2 x - 1$$

$$1 + \cos(2x) = 2 \cos^2 x$$

$$\frac{1 + \cos(2x)}{2} = \cos^2 x$$

Example 2. Derive $\cos^3 x = \frac{3\cos x + \cos(3x)}{4}$.

Solution. Begin with the triple angle formula (Chapter 6) for cosine:

$$\cos(3x) = 4\cos^3 x - 3\cos x$$
$$3\cos x + \cos(3x) = 4\cos^3 x$$
$$\frac{3\cos x + \cos(3x)}{4} = \cos^3 x$$

Chapter 7 Exercises

1. Derive $\sin^2 x = \frac{1 - \cos(2x)}{2}$.

2. Derive $\sin^3 x = \frac{3\sin x - \sin(3x)}{4}$.

3. Derive $\sin^4 x = \frac{3 - 4\cos(2x) + \cos(4x)}{8}$.

4. Derive $\cos^4 x = \frac{3 + 4\cos(2x) + \cos(4x)}{8}$.

5. Derive $\sin(5x) = 16\sin^5 x - 10\sin x + 5\sin(3x)$. (This problem is like Chapter 6.)

6. Use the answer to Problem 5 to derive $\sin^5 x = \frac{10 \sin x - 5 \sin(3x) + \sin(5x)}{16}$.

7. Derive $\cos(5x) = 16 \cos^5 x - 10 \cos x - 5 \cos(3x)$. (This problem is like Chapter 6.)

8. Use the answer to Problem 7 to derive $\cos^5 x = \frac{10\cos x + 5\cos(3x) + \cos(5x)}{16}$.

9. Derive $\tan^2 x = 1 - 2\frac{\tan x}{\tan(2x)}$.

10. Derive $\cot^2 x = 2\cot(2x)\cot x + 1$.

11. Derive $\tan^3 x = 3\tan x + 2\tan(3x) - 6\dfrac{\tan x \tan(3x)}{\tan(2x)}$.

12. Derive $\cot^3 x = 3\cot x + 2\cot(3x) + 6\cot x \cot(2x)\cot(3x)$.

13. Derive $\sec^2 x = \dfrac{2\sec(2x)}{\sec(2x)+1}$.

14. Derive $\csc^2 x = \dfrac{2\sec(2x)}{\sec(2x)-1}$.

15. Derive $\sec^3 x = 4\sec(3x) - 6\dfrac{\sec(2x)\sec(3x)}{\sec(2x)+1}$.

16. Derive $\csc^3 x = -4\csc(3x) + 6\dfrac{\sec(2x)\csc(3x)}{\sec(2x)-1}$.

8 Sum/Product Formulas

A product-to-sum identity solves for a product of two trig functions in terms of the sum or difference of two trig functions. Common examples include:

$$\sin x \sin y = \frac{\cos(x - y) - \cos(x + y)}{2}$$

$$\cos x \cos y = \frac{\cos(x - y) + \cos(x + y)}{2}$$

$$\sin x \cos y = \frac{\sin(x + y) + \sin(x - y)}{2}$$

$$\cos x \sin y = \frac{\sin(x + y) - \sin(x - y)}{2}$$

$$\tan x \tan y = \frac{\cos(x - y) - \cos(x + y)}{\cos(x - y) + \cos(x + y)}$$

$$\sec^2 x \csc^2 x = \sec^2 x + \csc^2 x$$

A sum-to-product identity solves for a sum or difference of two trig functions in terms of the product of two trig functions. Common examples include:

$$\sin x + \sin y = 2 \sin \left(\frac{x + y}{2}\right) \cos \left(\frac{x - y}{2}\right)$$

$$\sin x - \sin y = 2 \sin \left(\frac{x - y}{2}\right) \cos \left(\frac{x + y}{2}\right)$$

$$\cos x + \cos y = 2 \cos \left(\frac{x + y}{2}\right) \cos \left(\frac{x - y}{2}\right)$$

$$\cos x - \cos y = -2 \sin \left(\frac{x + y}{2}\right) \sin \left(\frac{x - y}{2}\right)$$

$$\sec^2 x + \csc^2 x = \sec^2 x \csc^2 x$$

Example 1. Show that $\sin x \sin y = \frac{\cos(x-y) - \cos(x+y)}{2}$.

Solution. Apply the sum and difference of angle formulas (Chapter 3) for cosine.

$$\frac{\cos(x - y) - \cos(x + y)}{2} = \frac{\cos x \cos y + \sin x \sin y - (\cos x \cos y - \sin x \sin y)}{2}$$

Distribute the minus sign. The two minus signs in the last term make a plus sign.

$$\frac{\cos(x - y) - \cos(x + y)}{2} = \frac{\cos x \cos y + \sin x \sin y - \cos x \cos y + \sin x \sin y}{2}$$

$$\frac{\cos(x - y) - \cos(x + y)}{2} = \frac{2 \sin x \sin y}{2} = \sin x \sin y$$

Example 2. Show that $\sin x + \sin y = 2 \sin \left(\frac{x+y}{2}\right) \cos \left(\frac{x-y}{2}\right)$.

Solution. Apply the sum and difference of angle formulas (Chapter 3).

$$2 \sin \left(\frac{x}{2} + \frac{y}{2}\right) \cos \left(\frac{x}{2} - \frac{y}{2}\right)$$

$$= 2 \left[\sin \left(\frac{x}{2}\right) \cos \left(\frac{y}{2}\right) + \sin \left(\frac{y}{2}\right) \cos \left(\frac{x}{2}\right)\right] \left[\cos \left(\frac{x}{2}\right) \cos \left(\frac{y}{2}\right) + \sin \left(\frac{x}{2}\right) \sin \left(\frac{y}{2}\right)\right]$$

Recall from algebra that $(a + b)(c + d) = ac + ad + bc + bd$.

$$2 \sin \left(\frac{x}{2} + \frac{y}{2}\right) \cos \left(\frac{x}{2} - \frac{y}{2}\right)$$

$$= 2 \sin \left(\frac{x}{2}\right) \cos \left(\frac{x}{2}\right) \cos^2 \left(\frac{y}{2}\right) + 2 \sin^2 \left(\frac{x}{2}\right) \cos \left(\frac{y}{2}\right) \sin \left(\frac{y}{2}\right) + 2 \sin \left(\frac{y}{2}\right) \cos^2 \left(\frac{x}{2}\right) \cos \left(\frac{y}{2}\right)$$

$$+ 2 \sin^2 \left(\frac{y}{2}\right) \cos \left(\frac{x}{2}\right) \sin \left(\frac{x}{2}\right)$$

We will reorder the terms, putting the last term second.

$$2 \sin \left(\frac{x}{2} + \frac{y}{2}\right) \cos \left(\frac{x}{2} - \frac{y}{2}\right)$$

$$= 2 \sin \left(\frac{x}{2}\right) \cos \left(\frac{x}{2}\right) \cos^2 \left(\frac{y}{2}\right) + 2 \sin^2 \left(\frac{y}{2}\right) \cos \left(\frac{x}{2}\right) \sin \left(\frac{x}{2}\right) + 2 \sin^2 \left(\frac{x}{2}\right) \cos \left(\frac{y}{2}\right) \sin \left(\frac{y}{2}\right)$$

$$+ 2 \sin \left(\frac{y}{2}\right) \cos^2 \left(\frac{x}{2}\right) \cos \left(\frac{y}{2}\right)$$

Factor out $2 \sin \left(\frac{x}{2}\right) \cos \left(\frac{x}{2}\right)$ in the first two terms and $\cos \left(\frac{y}{2}\right) \sin \left(\frac{y}{2}\right)$ in the last two terms.

$$2 \sin \left(\frac{x}{2} + \frac{y}{2}\right) \cos \left(\frac{x}{2} - \frac{y}{2}\right)$$

$$= 2 \sin \left(\frac{x}{2}\right) \cos \left(\frac{x}{2}\right) \left[\cos^2 \left(\frac{y}{2}\right) + \sin^2 \left(\frac{y}{2}\right)\right] + 2 \cos \left(\frac{y}{2}\right) \sin \left(\frac{y}{2}\right) \left[\sin^2 \left(\frac{x}{2}\right) + \cos^2 \left(\frac{x}{2}\right)\right]$$

Recognize that $\cos^2 \left(\frac{y}{2}\right) + \sin^2 \left(\frac{y}{2}\right) = 1$ and $\sin^2 \left(\frac{x}{2}\right) + \cos^2 \left(\frac{x}{2}\right)$. These are Pythagorean identities (Chapter 1).

$$2 \sin \left(\frac{x}{2} + \frac{y}{2}\right) \cos \left(\frac{x}{2} - \frac{y}{2}\right) = 2 \sin \left(\frac{x}{2}\right) \cos \left(\frac{x}{2}\right) + 2 \cos \left(\frac{y}{2}\right) \sin \left(\frac{y}{2}\right)$$

Now write the double angle formula (Chapter 4) for sine as $\sin(2z) = 2 \sin z \cos z$. Let $z = \frac{x}{2}$ such that $2z = x$ to see that $\sin x = 2 \sin \left(\frac{x}{2}\right) \cos \left(\frac{x}{2}\right)$ and similarly for y.

$$2 \sin \left(\frac{x}{2} + \frac{y}{2}\right) \cos \left(\frac{x}{2} - \frac{y}{2}\right) = \sin x + \sin y$$

Chapter 8 Exercises

1. Show that $\cos x \cos y = \frac{\cos(x-y)+\cos(x+y)}{2}$.

2. Show that $\sin x \cos y = \frac{\sin(x+y)+\sin(x-y)}{2}$.

3. Show that $\cos x \sin y = \dfrac{\sin(x+y)-\sin(x-y)}{2}$.

4. Show that $\tan x \tan y = \dfrac{\cos(x-y)-\cos(x+y)}{\cos(x-y)+\cos(x+y)}$.

5. Show that $\sec^2 x + \csc^2 x = \sec^2 x \csc^2 x$.

6. Show that $\sin x - \sin y = 2 \sin\left(\frac{x-y}{2}\right) \cos\left(\frac{x+y}{2}\right)$.

7. Show that $\cos x + \cos y = 2\cos\left(\frac{x+y}{2}\right)\cos\left(\frac{x-y}{2}\right)$.

8. Show that $\cos x - \cos y = -2\sin\left(\frac{x+y}{2}\right)\sin\left(\frac{x-y}{2}\right)$.

9 Angle Shifting Identities

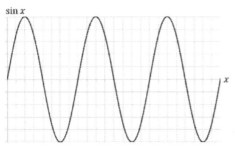
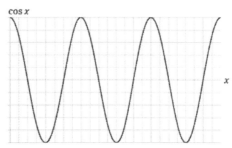

Graphs of sine and cosine look similar. The difference is that one graph is shifted $\frac{\pi}{2}$ rad (or 90°) compared to the other. Secant and cosecant are similarly shifted. Numerous trig identities relate to such shifts. There are also several trig identities that relate to the concept of reflection, since reflecting the graph of a trig function produces a new graph that is similar to the graphs of other trig functions. The trig identities in this section relate to angle shifts or reflections.

Some common angle shift or reflection identities include:

$$\sin(x + \pi) = -\sin x \quad , \quad \cos(x + \pi) = -\cos x$$
$$\csc(x + \pi) = -\csc x \quad , \quad \sec(x + \pi) = -\sec x$$
$$\tan(x + \pi) = \tan x \quad , \quad \cot(x + \pi) = \cot x$$
$$\sin\left(x \pm \frac{\pi}{2}\right) = \pm\cos x \quad , \quad \cos\left(x \pm \frac{\pi}{2}\right) = \mp\sin x$$
$$\csc\left(x \pm \frac{\pi}{2}\right) = \pm\sec x \quad , \quad \sec\left(x \pm \frac{\pi}{2}\right) = \mp\csc x$$
$$\tan\left(x + \frac{\pi}{2}\right) = -\cot x \quad , \quad \cot\left(x + \frac{\pi}{2}\right) = -\tan x$$
$$\sin(\pi - x) = \sin x \quad , \quad \cos(\pi - x) = -\cos x$$
$$\csc(\pi - x) = \csc x \quad , \quad \sec(\pi - x) = -\sec x$$
$$\tan(\pi - x) = -\tan x \quad , \quad \cot(\pi - x) = -\cot x$$
$$\sin\left(\frac{\pi}{2} - x\right) = \cos x \quad , \quad \cos\left(\frac{\pi}{2} - x\right) = \sin x$$
$$\csc\left(\frac{\pi}{2} - x\right) = \sec x \quad , \quad \sec\left(\frac{\pi}{2} - x\right) = \csc x$$
$$\tan\left(\frac{\pi}{2} - x\right) = \cot x \quad , \quad \cot\left(\frac{\pi}{2} - x\right) = \tan x$$

Recall from Chapter 2 that some trig functions are odd while others are even. This characteristic depends on whether a graph of the function is symmetric about the y-axis or if it is antisymmetric. We can express this characteristic as follows:

$$\sin(-x) = -\sin x \quad , \quad \cos(-x) = \cos x$$
$$\csc(-x) = -\csc x \quad , \quad \sec(-x) = \sec x$$
$$\tan(-x) = -\tan x \quad , \quad \cot(-x) = -\cot x$$

Example 1. Show that $\sin\left(\frac{\pi}{2} - x\right) = \cos x$.

Solution. Use the difference of angles formula (Chapter 3) for sine with $\frac{\pi}{2}$ for the first angle and x for the second angle.

$$\sin\left(\frac{\pi}{2} - x\right) = \sin\left(\frac{\pi}{2}\right)\cos x - \sin x \cos\left(\frac{\pi}{2}\right)$$

Recall that $\sin\left(\frac{\pi}{2}\right) = 1$ and $\cos\left(\frac{\pi}{2}\right) = 0$.

$$\sin\left(\frac{\pi}{2} - x\right) = (1)(\cos x) - (\sin x)(0) = \cos x$$

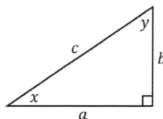

An alternative method is to consider the right triangle above. Note that $x + y = \frac{\pi}{2}$, such that $y = \frac{\pi}{2} - x$. For angle x, the adjacent is a, the opposite is b, and the hypotenuse is c, such that $\cos x = \frac{a}{c}$. For angle y, the adjacent is b, the opposite is a, and the hypotenuse is still c, such that $\sin y = \sin\left(\frac{\pi}{2} - x\right) = \frac{a}{c}$. Thus, we see that $\cos x = \sin\left(\frac{\pi}{2} - x\right)$. Note that $\frac{\pi}{2}$ rad corresponds to 90°.

Example 2. Show that $\sin(-x) = -\sin x$.

Solution. Since $0 - x = -x$, we may write $\sin(-x)$ as $\sin(0 - x)$. Use the difference of angles formula (Chapter 3) for sine with 0 for the first angle and x for the second angle.

$$\sin(0 - x) = \sin 0 \cos x - \sin x \cos 0$$

Recall that $\sin 0 = 0$ and $\cos 0 = 1$.

$$\sin(-x) = (0)(\cos x) - (\sin x)(1) = -\sin x$$

Chapter 9 Exercises

1. Show that $\sin(x + \pi) = -\sin x$.

2. Show that $\cos(x + \pi) = -\cos x$.

3. Show that $\csc(x + \pi) = -\csc x$.

4. Show that $\sec(x + \pi) = -\sec x$.

5. Show that $\tan(x + \pi) = \tan x$.

6. Show that $\cot(x + \pi) = \cot x$.

7. Show that $\sin\left(x \pm \frac{\pi}{2}\right) = \pm \cos x$.

8. Show that $\cos\left(x \pm \frac{\pi}{2}\right) = \mp \sin x$.

9. Show that $\tan\left(x + \frac{\pi}{2}\right) = -\cot x$.

10. Show that $\sin(\pi - x) = \sin x$.

11. Show that $\cos(\pi - x) = -\cos x$.

12. Show that $\tan(\pi - x) = -\tan x$.

13. Show that $\cos\left(\frac{\pi}{2} - x\right) = \sin x$.

14. Show that $\tan\left(\frac{\pi}{2} - x\right) = \cot x$.

15. Show that $\cos(-x) = \cos x$.

16. Show that $\tan(-x) = -\tan x$.

10 Law of Sines

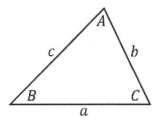

The <u>law of sines</u> relates a pair of sides and angles for any triangle, even if the triangle is acute or obtuse. This is a practical law for working with triangles. If we label the sides of a triangle a, b, and c and also label the angles A, B, and C such that uppercase letters are opposite to the respective lowercase letter (as shown above), the law of sines is

$$\frac{\sin A}{a} = \frac{\sin B}{b} = \frac{\sin C}{c}$$

Note that the law of sines may alternatively be expressed in terms of reciprocals:

$$\frac{a}{\sin A} = \frac{b}{\sin B} = \frac{c}{\sin C}$$

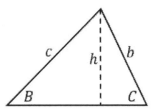

Example 1. Show that $\frac{\sin B}{b} = \frac{\sin C}{c}$.

Solution. Consider the triangle shown above. The dashed line of length h is the height of the triangle when the bottom side is interpreted as the base. The dashed line divides the triangle into two right triangles. In the left triangle, h is opposite to B and c is the hypotenuse. In the right triangle, h is opposite to C and b is the hypotenuse. The sines of B and C are therefore

$$\sin B = \frac{h}{c} \quad , \quad \sin C = \frac{h}{b}$$

Multiply both sides of the left equation by c and both sides of the right equation by b.

$$c \sin B = h \quad , \quad b \sin C = h$$

Since the right-hand side of each equation equals h, we may set the left-hand sides of these equations equal to one another.

$$c \sin B = b \sin C$$

Divide both sides of the equation by bc.

$$\frac{\sin B}{b} = \frac{\sin C}{c}$$

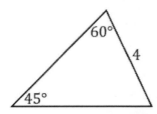

Example 2. Determine the length of the bottom side of the triangle above. (The diagram is **not** drawn to scale.)

Solution. First label the sides and angles of the triangle. The uppercase angles need to be opposite to the respective lowercase sides.

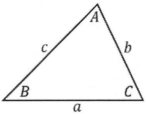

Identify the given information: $A = 60°$, $b = 4$, and $B = 45°$. Identify the unknown. We are looking for a. Plug numbers into $\frac{\sin A}{a} = \frac{\sin B}{b}$.

$$\frac{\sin 60°}{a} = \frac{\sin 45°}{4}$$

$$\frac{\sqrt{3}}{2a} = \frac{\sqrt{2}}{2(4)}$$

Cross multiply.

$$8\sqrt{3} = 2a\sqrt{2}$$

$$a = \frac{8\sqrt{3}}{2\sqrt{2}} = \frac{4\sqrt{3}}{\sqrt{2}} = \frac{4\sqrt{3}\,\sqrt{2}}{\sqrt{2}\,\sqrt{2}} = \frac{4\sqrt{6}}{2} = 2\sqrt{6}$$

We multiplied by $\frac{\sqrt{2}}{\sqrt{2}}$ in order to rationalize the denominator of $\frac{4\sqrt{3}}{\sqrt{2}}$. Our final answer is $a = 2\sqrt{6}$ units.

Chapter 10 Exercises

1. Show that $\frac{\sin A}{a} = \frac{\sin B}{b}$ for the triangle below.

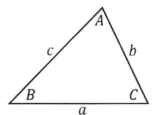

2. Directly show that $\frac{\sin A}{a} = \frac{\sin C}{c}$ for the triangle below.

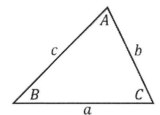

3. Show that $\frac{\sin B}{b} = \frac{\sin C}{c}$ for the obtuse triangle below.

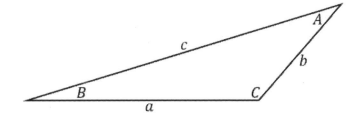

4. Show that if a triangle is inscribed in a circle with a diameter equal to d as shown below, $\frac{\sin A}{a} = \frac{\sin B}{b} = \frac{\sin C}{c} = \frac{1}{d}$.

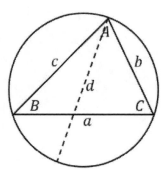

Notes: The diagrams are **not** drawn to scale. A calculator is **not** necessary.

5. Determine the length of the left side in the triangle below.

6. Determine the left interior angle in the triangle below.

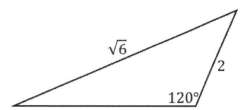

7. Determine the length of the bottom side in the triangle below.

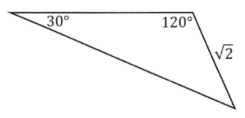

8. Determine the left interior angle in the triangle below.

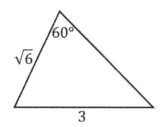

9. Determine the top interior angle in in the obtuse triangle below.

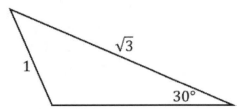

10. Determine the bottom interior angle in the triangle below.

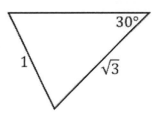

11. Determine the bottom interior angle in the triangle below.

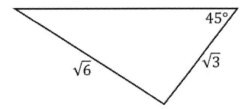

12. Determine the length of the top side in the triangle below.

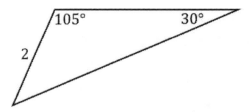

11 Law of Cosines

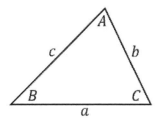

The **law of cosines** relates the three sides of any triangle, even if the triangle is acute or obtuse. It is a generalization of the Pythagorean theorem to a general triangle. This is a practical law for working with triangles. If we label the sides of a triangle a, b, and c and also label the angles A, B, and C such that uppercase letters are opposite to the respective lowercase letter (as shown above), the law of cosines may be written three different ways (once for each interior angle):

$$c^2 = a^2 + b^2 - 2ab \cos C$$
$$b^2 = a^2 + c^2 - 2ac \cos B$$
$$a^2 = b^2 + c^2 - 2bc \cos A$$

It is not necessary to be able to write the law of cosines in three different forms. For a given triangle, the form $c^2 = a^2 + b^2 - 2ab \cos C$ will work if you label the angle of interest C and its opposite side c.

How do you know when to apply the law of sines and when to apply the law of cosines? Look at which information you are given and what you are solving for:

- If you know all three sides, but do not know any angles, the law of cosines can help you solve for any of the angles.
- If you know one side and two of the angles (which really means that you know all three angles, since they add up to 180°), the law of sines can help you solve for either of the remaining sides.
- If you know two sides and one angle, if the angle that you know is opposite to one of the two sides that you know, the law of sines may be simpler, but the law of cosines will also work. If the angle that you know is not opposite to either of the sides that you know, use the law of cosines.

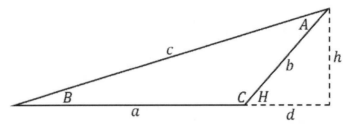

Example 1. Show that $c^2 = a^2 + b^2 - 2ab \cos C$ for the obtuse triangle shown above.

Solution. Draw the height of the triangle, as shown by the vertical dotted line. Note that the large triangle with sides $a + d$, h, and c is a right triangle. Apply the Pythagorean theorem to this large right triangle:

$$c^2 = (a + d)^2 + h^2$$

Multiply this out. Recall from algebra that $(a + d)^2 = a^2 + 2ad + d^2$.

$$c^2 = a^2 + 2ad + d^2 + h^2$$

The small triangle on the right with sides d, h, and b is also a right triangle. Apply the Pythagorean theorem to this small right triangle.

$$d^2 + h^2 = b^2$$

This allows us to replace $d^2 + h^2$ with b^2 in the previous equation.

$$c^2 = a^2 + 2ad + b^2$$

For the small right triangle, the cosine of angle H is

$$\cos H = \frac{d}{b}$$

Multiply both sides of this equation by b.

$$b \cos H = d$$

Substitute this expression for d into the equation $c^2 = a^2 + 2ad + b^2$.

$$c^2 = a^2 + 2ab \cos H + b^2$$

Note that angles C and H are supplementary: $C + H = \pi$ rad (or 180°), which may be expressed as $H = \pi - C$. Replace H with $\pi - C$ in the previous equation.

$$c^2 = a^2 + 2ab \cos(\pi - C) + b^2$$

Recall from Chapter 9 that $\cos(\pi - C) = -\cos C$.

$$c^2 = a^2 - 2ab \cos C + b^2$$

Rearrange the order of the terms.

$$c^2 = a^2 + b^2 - 2ab \cos C$$

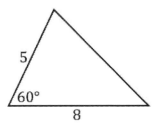

Example 2. Determine the length of the right side of the triangle above. (The diagram is **not** drawn to scale.)

Solution. Call the given angle $C = 60°$, the side opposite to it c, and the other sides $a = 8$ and $b = 5$. Apply the law of cosines.

$$c^2 = a^2 + b^2 - 2ab\cos C$$
$$c^2 = 8^2 + 5^2 - 2(8)(5)\cos 60°$$
$$c^2 = 64 + 25 - 80\left(\frac{1}{2}\right)$$
$$c^2 = 89 - 40$$
$$c^2 = 49$$
$$c = \sqrt{49} = 7$$

Chapter 11 Exercises

1. Show that $c^2 = a^2 + b^2 - 2ab\cos C$ for the triangle below.

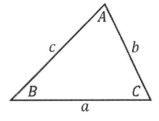

2. Show that when the law of cosines is applied to a right triangle with the right angle used as the angle, the law of cosines simplifies to the Pythagorean theorem.

Notes: The diagrams are **not** drawn to scale. A calculator is **not** necessary.

3. Determine the bottom right interior angle in the triangle below.

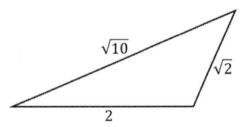

4. Determine the length of the right side in the triangle below.

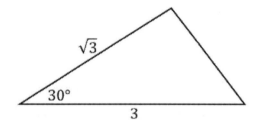

5. Determine the length of the bottom side in the triangle below.

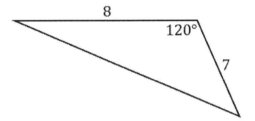

6. Determine the bottom right interior angle in the triangle below.

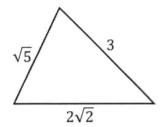

7. Determine the length of the bottom left side in the triangle below.

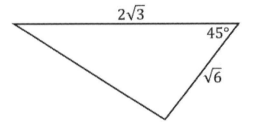

8. Determine the bottom left interior angle in the triangle below.

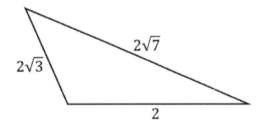

9. Determine the length of the top side in the triangle below.

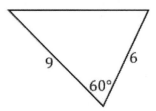

10. Determine the top right interior angle in the triangle below.

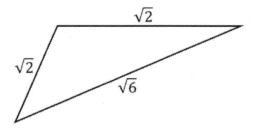

11. Determine the top interior angle in the triangle below.

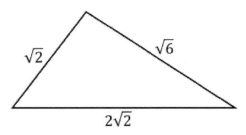

12. Determine the length of the bottom side in the triangle below.

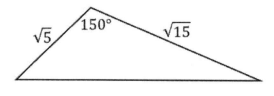

12 Inverse Function Identities

We use the notation $\sin^{-1} x$ to represent an **inverse** trig function. (Note that this is **not** a reciprocal or exponent.) For example, the inverse sine function, $\sin^{-1} x$, asks the question, "What angle can you take the sine of and get x as the answer?" For example, $\sin^{-1}\left(\frac{1}{2}\right)$ equals $30°$ or $150°$ because $\sin 30° = \frac{1}{2}$ and $\sin 150° = \frac{1}{2}$.

(Some books and instructors use arcsine notation instead, written as $\text{asin}\, x$. An arcsine means inverse sine: $\text{asin}\, x = \sin^{-1} x$.)

An inverse trig function is effectively the opposite to its corresponding trig function, as indicated by the following identities. Note that there are generally two answers to an inverse trig function within the four quadrants. For example, $\sin^{-1}(\sin x)$ has two answers, x or $\pi - x$, because there are generally two answers to the inverse sine. For example, if $x = \frac{\pi}{6}$, we get $\sin^{-1}\left[\sin\left(\frac{\pi}{6}\right)\right] = \sin^{-1}\left(\frac{1}{2}\right)$, which has two answers, $\frac{\pi}{6}$ or $\frac{5\pi}{6}$, because $\sin\left(\frac{\pi}{6}\right) = \frac{1}{2}$ and $\sin\left(\frac{5\pi}{6}\right) = \frac{1}{2}$. Also note that you may add or subtract 2π rad to an inverse trig function and obtain an equivalent answer. For example, $\sin^{-1}\left[\sin\left(\frac{\pi}{6}\right)\right]$ could also be $\frac{\pi}{6} + 2\pi = \frac{13\pi}{6}$ or $\frac{\pi}{6} - 2\pi = -\frac{11\pi}{6}$, or even $\frac{\pi}{6} + 4\pi = \frac{25\pi}{6}$. Adding 2π rad is the equivalent of going full circle.

$$\sin(\sin^{-1} x) = x \quad , \quad \sin^{-1}(\sin x) = x \text{ or } \pi - x$$
$$\cos(\cos^{-1} x) = x \quad , \quad \cos^{-1}(\cos x) = x \text{ or } 2\pi - x \text{ (or} - x)$$
$$\tan(\tan^{-1} x) = x \quad , \quad \tan^{-1}(\tan x) = x \text{ or } x \pm \pi$$
$$\cot(\cot^{-1} x) = x \quad , \quad \cot^{-1}(\cot x) = x \text{ or } x \pm \pi$$
$$\sec(\sec^{-1} x) = x \quad , \quad \sec^{-1}(\sec x) = x \text{ or } 2\pi - x \text{ (or} - x)$$
$$\csc(\csc^{-1} x) = x \quad , \quad \csc^{-1}(\csc x) = x \text{ or } \pi - x$$

The identities below apply to **principal values**: $-\frac{\pi}{2} \leq \theta \leq \frac{\pi}{2}$ for $\sin\theta$, $\tan\theta$, and $\csc\theta$, $0 \leq \theta \leq \pi$ for $\cos\theta$, $\cot\theta$, and $\sec\theta$ (excluding undefined values like $\theta = 0$ for $\csc\theta$).

$$\sin^{-1} x + \cos^{-1} x = \sec^{-1} x + \csc^{-1} x = \frac{\pi}{2} \quad \text{(for principal values)}$$

$$\tan^{-1} x + \cot^{-1} x = \frac{\pi}{2} \quad \text{(if } x > 0) \quad , \quad \tan^{-1} x + \cot^{-1} x = -\frac{\pi}{2} \quad \text{(if } x < 0)$$

When an inverse trig function is combined with a different trig function, we get the following identities.

$$\sin(\cos^{-1} x) = \sqrt{1 - x^2} \quad , \quad \cos(\sin^{-1} x) = \sqrt{1 - x^2}$$

$$\sin(\tan^{-1} x) = \frac{x}{\sqrt{1 + x^2}} \quad , \quad \tan(\sin^{-1} x) = \frac{x}{\sqrt{1 - x^2}}$$

$$\cos(\tan^{-1} x) = \frac{1}{\sqrt{1 + x^2}} \quad , \quad \tan(\cos^{-1} x) = \frac{\sqrt{1 - x^2}}{x}$$

$$\sin(\cot^{-1} x) = \frac{1}{\sqrt{1 + x^2}} \quad , \quad \cot(\sin^{-1} x) = \frac{\sqrt{1 - x^2}}{x}$$

$$\cos(\cot^{-1} x) = \frac{x}{\sqrt{1 + x^2}} \quad , \quad \cot(\cos^{-1} x) = \frac{x}{\sqrt{1 - x^2}}$$

$$\tan(\cot^{-1} x) = \frac{1}{x} \quad , \quad \cot(\tan^{-1} x) = \frac{1}{x} \quad , \quad \cos(\sec^{-1} x) = \frac{1}{x}$$

$$\sec(\cos^{-1} x) = \frac{1}{x} \quad , \quad \sin(\csc^{-1} x) = \frac{1}{x} \quad , \quad \csc(\sin^{-1} x) = \frac{1}{x}$$

$$\sin(\sec^{-1} x) = \frac{\sqrt{x^2 - 1}}{x} \quad , \quad \sec(\sin^{-1} x) = \frac{1}{\sqrt{1 - x^2}}$$

$$\cos(\csc^{-1} x) = \frac{\sqrt{x^2 - 1}}{x} \quad , \quad \csc(\cos^{-1} x) = \frac{1}{\sqrt{1 - x^2}}$$

$$\sec(\csc^{-1} x) = \frac{x}{\sqrt{x^2 - 1}} \quad , \quad \csc(\sec^{-1} x) = \frac{x}{\sqrt{x^2 - 1}}$$

$$\sec(\tan^{-1} x) = \sqrt{1 + x^2} \quad , \quad \tan(\sec^{-1} x) = \sqrt{x^2 - 1}$$

$$\csc(\tan^{-1} x) = \frac{\sqrt{1 + x^2}}{x} \quad , \quad \tan(\csc^{-1} x) = \frac{1}{\sqrt{x^2 - 1}}$$

$$\sec(\cot^{-1} x) = \frac{\sqrt{1 + x^2}}{x} \quad , \quad \cot(\sec^{-1} x) = \frac{1}{\sqrt{x^2 - 1}}$$

$$\csc(\cot^{-1} x) = \sqrt{1 + x^2} \quad , \quad \cot(\csc^{-1} x) = \sqrt{x^2 - 1}$$

Standard sum and difference formulas for inverse trig functions include:

$$\sin^{-1} x \pm \sin^{-1} y = \sin^{-1}\left(x\sqrt{1 - y^2} \pm y\sqrt{1 - x^2}\right)$$

$$\cos^{-1} x \pm \cos^{-1} y = \cos^{-1}\left(xy \mp \sqrt{(1 - x^2)(1 - y^2)}\right)$$

$$\tan^{-1} x \pm \tan^{-1} y = \tan^{-1}\left(\frac{x \pm y}{1 \mp xy}\right)$$

$$\cot^{-1} x \pm \cot^{-1} y = \cot^{-1}\left(\frac{xy \mp 1}{y \pm x}\right)$$

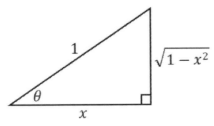

Example 1. Show that $\sin(\cos^{-1} x) = \sqrt{1 - x^2}$.

Solution. Since cosine is adjacent over hypotenuse, draw a right triangle where the adjacent of θ is x and the hypotenuse is 1, like the diagram above. The reason behind this is that $\cos \theta = \frac{x}{1} = x$, such that $\cos^{-1} x = \theta$. Substitute this into $\sin(\cos^{-1} x)$:

$$\sin(\cos^{-1} x) = \sin \theta$$

Apply the Pythagorean theorem to determine that the opposite to θ is $\sqrt{1 - x^2}$. Since sine is opposite over hypotenuse,

$$\sin(\cos^{-1} x) = \sin \theta = \frac{\sqrt{1 - x^2}}{1} = \sqrt{1 - x^2}$$

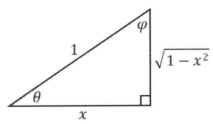

Example 2. Show that $\sin^{-1} x + \cos^{-1} x = \frac{\pi}{2}$ for the right triangle of Example 1.

Solution. We will use the same right triangle as we used in Example 1, except that we will also label the second acute interior angle φ. As with Example 1, $\cos^{-1} x = \theta$ and the side opposite to θ is $\sqrt{1 - x^2}$. Note that x is opposite to the second angle φ, such that $\sin \varphi = \frac{x}{1} = x$, for which it follows that $\sin^{-1} x = \varphi$. Substitute $\cos^{-1} x = \theta$ and $\sin^{-1} x = \varphi$ into the sum of inverse sine and inverse cosine.

$$\sin^{-1} x + \cos^{-1} x = \theta + \varphi$$

Since θ, φ, and the right angle add up to π rad (or 180°), it follows that

$$\theta + \varphi = \frac{\pi}{2}$$

This completes the proof. On the next page, we have a few notes.

Compare and contrast. For the first angle, $\cos\theta = x$ while $\sin\theta = \sqrt{1-x^2}$, whereas for the second angle, $\sin\varphi = x$ and $\cos\varphi = \sqrt{1-x^2}$. We noted what is effectively the same result in the alternate solution to Example 1 in Chapter 9. This identity basically states that the two acute angles in a right triangle add up to $\frac{\pi}{2}$ rad (or 90°), or that the sine of an angle is the same as the cosine of its complement (and vice-versa).

Example 3. Show that $\sin^{-1}x \pm \sin^{-1}y = \sin^{-1}\left(x\sqrt{1-y^2} \pm y\sqrt{1-x^2}\right)$.
Solution. Begin with the sum of angle identity for sine from Chapter 3 expressed in terms of θ and φ.
$$\sin(\theta \pm \varphi) = \sin\theta\cos\varphi \pm \sin\varphi\cos\theta$$
Take the inverse sine of both sides.
$$\sin^{-1}[\sin(\theta \pm \varphi)] = \sin^{-1}(\sin\theta\cos\varphi \pm \sin\varphi\cos\theta)$$
The left-hand side simplifies to $\theta \pm \varphi$ (or its alternate angle in another quadrant for which sine has the same sign; it is simpler to restrict this to the principal values from the bottom of page 63).
$$\theta \pm \varphi = \sin^{-1}(\sin\theta\cos\varphi \pm \sin\varphi\cos\theta)$$

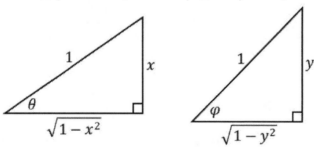

Since sine is opposite over hypotenuse, draw a right triangle where the opposite of θ is x and the hypotenuse is 1, and another right triangle where the opposite of φ is y and the hypotenuse is 1. The reason behind this is that $\sin\theta = \frac{x}{1} = x$ and $\sin\varphi = \frac{y}{1} = y$, such that $\theta = \sin^{-1}x$ and $\varphi = \sin^{-1}y$. According to the Pythagorean theorem, $\sqrt{1-x^2}$ is adjacent to θ and $\sqrt{1-y^2}$ is adjacent to φ, such that $\cos\theta = \frac{\sqrt{1-x^2}}{1} = \sqrt{1-x^2}$ and $\cos\varphi = \frac{\sqrt{1-y^2}}{1} = \sqrt{1-y^2}$. Substitute these expressions into the previous equation.
$$\sin^{-1}x \pm \sin^{-1}y = \sin^{-1}\left(x\sqrt{1-y^2} \pm y\sqrt{1-x^2}\right)$$

Chapter 12 Exercises

1. Show that $\sin(\sin^{-1} x) = x$, $\cos(\sin^{-1} x) = \sqrt{1 - x^2}$, $\tan(\sin^{-1} x) = \frac{x}{\sqrt{1-x^2}}$, $\cot(\sin^{-1} x) = \frac{\sqrt{1-x^2}}{x}$, $\sec(\sin^{-1} x) = \frac{1}{\sqrt{1-x^2}}$, and $\csc(\sin^{-1} x) = \frac{1}{x}$.

2. Show that $\sin(\cos^{-1} x) = \sqrt{1 - x^2}$, $\cos(\cos^{-1} x) = x$, $\tan(\cos^{-1} x) = \frac{\sqrt{1-x^2}}{x}$, $\cot(\cos^{-1} x) = \frac{x}{\sqrt{1-x^2}}$, $\sec(\cos^{-1} x) = \frac{1}{x}$, and $\csc(\cos^{-1} x) = \frac{1}{\sqrt{1-x^2}}$.

3. Show that $\sin(\tan^{-1} x) = \frac{x}{\sqrt{1+x^2}}$, $\cos(\tan^{-1} x) = \frac{1}{\sqrt{1+x^2}}$, $\tan(\tan^{-1} x) = x$,

$\cot(\tan^{-1} x) = \frac{1}{x}$, $\sec(\tan^{-1} x) = \sqrt{1 + x^2}$, and $\csc(\tan^{-1} x) = \frac{\sqrt{1+x^2}}{x}$.

4. Show that $\sin(\cot^{-1} x) = \frac{1}{\sqrt{1+x^2}}$, $\cos(\cot^{-1} x) = \frac{x}{\sqrt{1+x^2}}$, $\tan(\cot^{-1} x) = \frac{1}{x}$, $\cot(\cot^{-1} x) = x$, $\sec(\cot^{-1} x) = \frac{\sqrt{1+x^2}}{x}$, and $\csc(\cot^{-1} x) = \sqrt{1+x^2}$.

5. Show that $\sin(\sec^{-1} x) = \frac{\sqrt{x^2-1}}{x}$, $\cos(\sec^{-1} x) = \frac{1}{x}$, $\tan(\sec^{-1} x) = \sqrt{x^2 - 1}$,

$\cot(\sec^{-1} x) = \frac{1}{\sqrt{x^2-1}}$, $\sec(\sec^{-1} x) = x$, and $\csc(\sec^{-1} x) = \frac{x}{\sqrt{x^2-1}}$.

6. Show that $\sin(\csc^{-1} x) = \frac{1}{x}$, $\cos(\csc^{-1} x) = \frac{\sqrt{x^2-1}}{x}$, $\tan(\csc^{-1} x) = \frac{1}{\sqrt{x^2-1}}$, $\cot(\csc^{-1} x) = \sqrt{x^2-1}$, $\sec(\csc^{-1} x) = \frac{x}{\sqrt{x^2-1}}$, and $\csc(\csc^{-1} x) = x$.

7. Show that $\sec^{-1} x + \csc^{-1} x = \frac{\pi}{2}$ for a right triangle suitable to Problem 5.

8. Show that $\tan^{-1} x + \cot^{-1} x = \frac{\pi}{2}$ for a right triangle suitable to Problem 3.

9. Show that $\cos^{-1} x \pm \cos^{-1} y = \cos^{-1}\left(xy \mp \sqrt{(1 - x^2)(1 - y^2)}\right)$.

10. Show that $\tan^{-1} x \pm \tan^{-1} y = \tan^{-1}\left(\frac{x \pm y}{1 \mp xy}\right)$.

11. Show that $\cot^{-1} x \pm \cot^{-1} y = \cot^{-1}\left(\frac{xy \mp 1}{y \pm x}\right)$.

12. Use an inverse identity to find $\sin^{-1}\left(\sin\frac{\pi}{3}\right)$.

13. Use an inverse identity to find $\sin(\cos^{-1}0.6)$.

14. Use an inverse identity to find $\tan\left(\sin^{-1}\frac{1}{3}\right)$.

15. Use an inverse identity to find $\cos^{-1}\left(\cos\frac{2\pi}{3}\right)$.

16. Use an inverse identity to find $\sec(\tan^{-1}2)$.

17. Use an inverse identity to find $\csc(\cot^{-1}3)$.

18. Use an inverse identity to find $\tan^{-1}\left[\tan\left(-\frac{\pi}{6}\right)\right]$.

19. Use an inverse identity to find $\cos(\sec^{-1}1.5)$.

20. Use an inverse identity to find $\cot\left(\sin^{-1}\frac{3}{4}\right)$.

21. Use an inverse identity to find $\sec(\csc^{-1}5)$.

13 Applications

The problems in this chapter apply identities from Chapters 1-12.

Chapter 13 Exercises

1. A vector has the following components.
$$A_x = A \cos \theta$$
$$A_y = A \sin \theta$$
Show that the magnitude and direction of the vector are
$$A = \sqrt{A_x^2 + A_y^2}$$
$$\theta = \tan^{-1}\left(\frac{A_y}{A_x}\right)$$

2. In 2D polar coordinates,

$$r = \sqrt{x^2 + y^2}$$
$$\theta = \tan^{-1}\left(\frac{y}{x}\right)$$

Show that

$$x = r\cos\theta$$
$$y = r\sin\theta$$

3. In spherical coordinates,

$$x = r \cos \theta \sin \varphi$$
$$y = r \sin \theta \sin \varphi$$
$$z = r \cos \varphi$$

Show that

$$r = \sqrt{x^2 + y^2 + z^2}$$
$$\varphi = \cos^{-1}\left(\frac{z}{\sqrt{x^2 + y^2 + z^2}}\right)$$
$$\theta = \tan^{-1}\left(\frac{y}{x}\right)$$

Note: This is the notation used in many math books. In physics books, θ and φ are often reversed compared to math books.

4. A projectile traveling through a uniform gravitational field satisfies the equations

$$x = v_0 t \cos \theta_0$$

$$y = v_0 \sin \theta_0 \, t - \frac{1}{2} g t^2$$

If the net vertical displacement is $y = 0$, the horizontal displacement is called the range and is denoted $x = R$. Show that in this case

$$R = \frac{v_0^2}{g} \sin(2\theta_0)$$

Show that the range is a maximum when the launch angle is $\theta_0 = \frac{\pi}{4}$ rad (or $45°$).

5. A girl ties a small rock to a string and twirls the free end of the string in such a way that the rock rotates in a horizontal circle with constant speed. When she does this, the string makes an angle θ with the vertical. (Note: The *rock* travels in a horizontal circle, but the *string* is **not** horizontal. The string traces out the surface of a cone.) The tension (T) in the string satisfies the following equations.

$$T \cos \theta = mg$$

$$T \sin \theta = \frac{mv^2}{R}$$

Show that the tension equals

$$T = m \sqrt{g^2 + \frac{v^4}{R^2}}$$

and that the angle in the cord satisfies

$$\theta = \tan^{-1} \left(\frac{v^2}{Rg} \right)$$

6. A physics student draws three vectors that are joined tip-to-tail, as shown below.

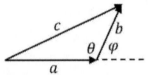

The two joined vectors have magnitudes of a and b, while the resultant vector has a magnitude of c. The physics student states that the magnitudes of the vectors are related by the following equation, where φ is the angle between the two joined vectors.

$$c^2 = a^2 + b^2 + 2ab \cos \varphi$$

A math student points out that the law of cosines for this triangle has a minus sign, not a plus sign.

$$c^2 = a^2 + b^2 - 2ab \cos \theta$$

Show that both students are correct.

7. A physics student derives the following formula for a block sliding down an incline with friction.

$$a = g\left(\cos\alpha - \mu\sin\alpha\right)$$

When the student checks the answer in the back of the book, the formula is

$$a = g\left(\sin\theta - \mu\cos\theta\right)$$

Show that both answers can be correct if α and θ are the two acute interior angles of a right triangle.

8. A spring oscillates with simple harmonic motion according to the equation
$$y = A\cos(\omega t + \varphi)$$
Show that this equation can equivalently be expressed as
$$y = D\cos(\omega t) + E\sin(\omega t)$$
provided that

$$A = \sqrt{D^2 + E^2}$$
$$\varphi = \tan^{-1}\left(-\frac{E}{D}\right)$$

Assume that $D > 0$.

9. One way to compute π numerically is to use the following formula.

$$\frac{\pi}{4} = \tan^{-1}\left(\frac{1}{2}\right) + \tan^{-1}\left(\frac{1}{3}\right)$$

Show that this formula is correct.

10. Two waves traveling in the same medium with slightly different frequencies have displacements given by

$$y_1 = A\cos(2\pi f_1 t) \quad , \quad y_2 = A\cos(2\pi f_2 t)$$

According to the superposition principle, the resulting displacement is $y = y_1 + y_2$. Show that

$$y = 2A\cos(\pi f_b t)\cos(2\pi f_a t)$$

The resulting displacement has an amplitude, $2A\cos(2\pi f_a t)$, which varies in time with an average frequency of $f_a = \frac{f_1 + f_2}{2}$. The beat frequency, $f_b = |f_1 - f_2|$, is the frequency with which the maxima of the amplitude are observed.

HINTS AND ANSWERS

Chapter 1 Pythagorean Identities

1. Answer: $\tan^2 x + 1 = \sec^2 x$

Hints: One method is to solve this problem like Example 1, but divide both sides of the Pythagorean theorem by a^2 (instead of c^2). An alternative method is to divide by $\cos^2 x$ on both sides of $\sin^2 x + \cos^2 x = 1$.

2. Answer: $1 + \cot^2 x = \csc^2 x$

Hints: One method is to solve this problem like Example 1, but divide both sides of the Pythagorean theorem by b^2 (instead of c^2). An alternative method is to divide by $\sin^2 x$ on both sides of $\sin^2 x + \cos^2 x = 1$.

3. Answer: $\sin x = \pm\sqrt{1 - \cos^2 x}$

Hint: Isolate $\sin x$ in the identity $\sin^2 x + \cos^2 x = 1$.

4. Answer: $\sec x = \pm\sqrt{1 + \tan^2 x}$

Hint: Square root both sides of $\tan^2 x + 1 = \sec^2 x$.

5. Answer: $\tan x = \pm\dfrac{\sin x}{\sqrt{1 - \sin^2 x}}$

Hints: Start with $\tan x = \dfrac{\sin x}{\cos x}$. Isolate $\cos x$ in the identity $\sin^2 x + \cos^2 x = 1$.

6. Answer: $\sin x = \pm\dfrac{\sqrt{\sec^2 x - 1}}{\sec x}$

Hints: Start with $\tan^2 x + 1 = \sec^2 x$. Show that $\tan x = \pm\sqrt{\sec^2 x - 1}$ (similar to the solutions to Problems 3-4). Note: $\tan x = \dfrac{\sin x}{\cos x} = \sin x \sec x$ such that $\sin x = \dfrac{\tan x}{\sec x}$.

7. Answer: $\csc x = \pm\dfrac{\sqrt{1 + \tan^2 x}}{\tan x}$

Hints: First show that $\csc x = \dfrac{\sec x}{\tan x}$. Now use the formula from Problem 4.

8. Answer: $\tan x = \pm\dfrac{1}{\sqrt{\csc^2 x - 1}}$

Hints: Start with $1 + \cot^2 x = \csc^2 x$. Show that $\cot x = \pm\sqrt{\csc^2 x - 1}$ (similar to the solutions to Problems 3-4). Take the reciprocal of both sides. Note that $\dfrac{1}{\cot x} = \tan x$.

9. Answers: $\cos x = \pm\dfrac{4}{5} = \pm 0.8$

Hint: Isolate $\cos x$ in the identity $\sin^2 x + \cos^2 x = 1$ (like in the solution to Problem 5.)

Check: $\sin^2 x + \cos^2 x = (0.6)^2 + (\pm 0.8)^2 = 0.36 + 0.64 = 1$

10. Answers: $\tan x = \pm \frac{12}{5} = \pm 2.4$

Hints: One method is to use the result of Example 2. An alternative method is to use the formula from Problem 3 to find $\sin x$ and then use $\tan x = \frac{\sin x}{\cos x}$.

Check: $\sin x = \tan x \cos x = \left(\pm \frac{12}{5}\right)\left(\frac{5}{13}\right) = \pm \frac{12}{13}$ and

$\sin^2 x + \cos^2 x = \left(\pm \frac{12}{13}\right)^2 + \left(\frac{5}{13}\right)^2 = \frac{144}{169} + \frac{25}{169} = \frac{169}{169} = 1$

11. Answers: $\cos x = \pm \frac{2}{3}$

Hints: One method is to first show that $\cos x = \pm \frac{1}{\sqrt{1+\tan^2 x}}$. An alternative method is to use the formula from Problem 4 to find $\sec x$ and then use $\sec x = \frac{1}{\cos x}$.

Check: $\sin x = \tan x \cos x = \left(\frac{\sqrt{5}}{2}\right)\left(\pm \frac{2}{3}\right) = \pm \frac{\sqrt{5}}{3}$ and

$\sin^2 x + \cos^2 x = \left(\pm \frac{\sqrt{5}}{3}\right)^2 + \left(\pm \frac{2}{3}\right)^2 = \frac{5}{9} + \frac{4}{9} = \frac{9}{9} = 1$

12. Answers: $\cot x = \pm \frac{7}{\sqrt{15}}$ If you rationalize the denominator, you get $\pm \frac{7\sqrt{15}}{15}$.

Hint: First show that $\cot x = \pm \frac{1}{\sqrt{\sec^2 x - 1}}$.

Check: $\tan x = \frac{1}{\cot x} = \pm \frac{\sqrt{15}}{7}$ and $\tan^2 x + 1 = \left(\pm \frac{\sqrt{15}}{7}\right)^2 + 1 = \frac{15}{49} + \frac{49}{49} = \frac{64}{49}$, which agrees

with $\sec^2 x = \left(\frac{8}{7}\right)^2 = \frac{64}{49}$.

13. Answers: $x = \frac{\pi}{4}, \frac{3\pi}{4}, \frac{5\pi}{4}$, or $\frac{7\pi}{4}$ rad (corresponding to $45°$, $135°$, $225°$, or $315°$)

Hints: Use the identity $\sin^2 x + \cos^2 x = 1$ to write $\sin^2 x = 1 - \cos^2 x$. Plug this into the given equation to get $5 - 8\cos^2 x = 1$. Isolate the cosine function and take the inverse cosine of both sides. There is a $\pm$ when you square root both sides, and for each sign the inverse cosine has a solution in two different quadrants, giving a total of four possible answers.

Check: $5\sin^2\left(\frac{\pi}{4}\right) - 3\cos^2\left(\frac{\pi}{4}\right) = 5\left(\frac{1}{\sqrt{2}}\right)^2 - 3\left(\frac{1}{\sqrt{2}}\right)^2 = \frac{5}{2} - \frac{3}{2} = \frac{2}{2} = 1$,

$5\sin^2\left(\frac{3\pi}{4}\right) - 3\cos^2\left(\frac{3\pi}{4}\right) = 5\left(\frac{1}{\sqrt{2}}\right)^2 - 3\left(-\frac{1}{\sqrt{2}}\right)^2 = \frac{5}{2} - \frac{3}{2} = \frac{2}{2} = 1$,

$5\sin^2\left(\frac{5\pi}{4}\right) - 3\cos^2\left(\frac{5\pi}{4}\right) = 5\left(-\frac{1}{\sqrt{2}}\right)^2 - 3\left(-\frac{1}{\sqrt{2}}\right)^2 = \frac{5}{2} - \frac{3}{2} = \frac{2}{2} = 1$,

and $5\sin^2\left(\frac{7\pi}{4}\right) - 3\cos^2\left(\frac{7\pi}{4}\right) = 5\left(-\frac{1}{\sqrt{2}}\right)^2 - 3\left(\frac{1}{\sqrt{2}}\right)^2 = \frac{5}{2} - \frac{3}{2} = \frac{2}{2} = 1$

14. Answers: $x = \frac{\pi}{3}, \frac{2\pi}{3}, \frac{4\pi}{3}$, or $\frac{5\pi}{3}$ rad (corresponding to $60°, 120°, 240°$, or $300°$)

Hints: One method is to add $\sin^2 x$ to both sides and then factor out $\sin^2 x$. Now use the identity $\tan^2 x + 1 = \sec^2 x$. Note that $\sin x \sec x = \frac{\sin x}{\cos x} = \tan x$. Isolate the tangent function and take the inverse tangent of both sides. There are four possible angles, similar to the solution to Problem 13. An alternative method is to use the identity from Problem 5 and apply algebra to isolate the sine function.

Check: $\sin^2 x \tan^2 x = \sin^2\left(\frac{\pi}{3}\right)\tan^2\left(\frac{\pi}{3}\right) = \left(\frac{\sqrt{3}}{2}\right)^2 (\sqrt{3})^2 = \left(\frac{3}{4}\right)(3) = \frac{9}{4}$ agrees with

$3 - \sin^2 x = 3 - \sin^2\left(\frac{\pi}{3}\right) = 3 - \left(\frac{\sqrt{3}}{2}\right)^2 = 3 - \frac{3}{4} = \frac{12}{4} - \frac{3}{4} = \frac{9}{4}$

The other angles yield the same results; the difference is that there will be squared minus signs (like the check for the solution to Problem 13), but squaring a minus sign has no effect.

15. Answers: $x = \frac{\pi}{3}$ or $\frac{2\pi}{3}$ rad (corresponding to $60°$ or $120°$)

Hints: Use the identity $\sin^2 x + \cos^2 x = 1$ to write $\cos^2 x = 1 - \sin^2 x$. Plug this into the given equation to get $\sin x - \sqrt{3} + \sqrt{3}\sin^2 x = \frac{\sqrt{3}}{4}$. (Remember to distribute the minus sign.) Now define $y = \sin^2 x$ to get an equation that is quadratic in y; solve the quadratic to find y and use the real answer to determine x. There is one real value for y, and there are two real values for the inverse sine, yielding two real answers.

Check: $\sin x - \sqrt{3}\cos^2 x = \sin\left(\frac{\pi}{3}\right) - \sqrt{3}\cos^2\left(\frac{\pi}{3}\right) = \frac{\sqrt{3}}{2} - \sqrt{3}\left(\frac{1}{2}\right)^2 = \frac{\sqrt{3}}{2} - \frac{\sqrt{3}}{4} = \frac{\sqrt{3}}{4}$ and

$\sin x - \sqrt{3}\cos^2 x = \sin\left(\frac{2\pi}{3}\right) - \sqrt{3}\cos^2\left(\frac{2\pi}{3}\right) = \frac{\sqrt{3}}{2} - \sqrt{3}\left(-\frac{1}{2}\right)^2 = \frac{\sqrt{3}}{2} - \frac{\sqrt{3}}{4} = \frac{\sqrt{3}}{4}$

16. Answers: $x = \frac{2\pi}{3}$ or $\frac{4\pi}{3}$ rad (corresponding to $120°$ or $240°$)

Hints: Subtract $\sqrt{3}$ from both sides to get $\tan x = 2 - \sqrt{3} + \sec x$. Square both sides. This similar to the foil method (distributive property) of algebra on the right-hand side, except that there will be more than 4 terms. You should get:

$$\tan^2 x = 4 - 4\sqrt{3} + 3 + \sec^2 x + 4\sec x - 2\sqrt{3}\sec x$$

Substitute $\tan^2 x = \sec^2 x - 1$ on the left-hand side. In this problem, $\sec^2 x$ cancels out. Isolate $\sec x$. Note that $-\left(4 - 2\sqrt{3}\right)\sec x = 8 - 4\sqrt{3}$ simplifies to $\sec x = -2$ since $8 - 4\sqrt{3} = -2\left(4 - 2\sqrt{3}\right)$ such that $\sec x = \frac{8 - 4\sqrt{3}}{4 - 2\sqrt{3}} = -2$. Take the inverse secant on both sides. There will be two answers, one in Quadrant II and one in Quadrant III (because secant is negative in Quadrants II and III).

Check: $\sqrt{3} + \tan\left(\frac{2\pi}{3}\right) = \sqrt{3} - \sqrt{3} = 0$ agrees with $2 + \sec\left(\frac{2\pi}{3}\right) = 2 - 2 = 0$ and $\sqrt{3} + \tan\left(\frac{4\pi}{3}\right) = \sqrt{3} - \sqrt{3} = 0$ agrees with $2 + \sec\left(\frac{4\pi}{3}\right) = 2 - 2 = 0$

Chapter 2 Odd and Even Functions

1. Answer: $\tan(-\theta) = -\tan\theta$

Hints: One method is to show that $x \to x$ and $y \to -y$ when $\theta \to -\theta$, such that $\frac{y}{x} \to -\frac{y}{x}$. An alternative method is to begin with $\tan\theta = \frac{\sin\theta}{\cos\theta}$ and use $\sin(-\theta) = -\sin\theta$ and $\cos(-\theta) = \cos\theta$.

2. Answer: $\sec(-\theta) = \sec\theta$

Hint: Since $\sec\theta = \frac{1}{\cos\theta}$, the solution is similar to Example 2 except that $\sec\theta = \frac{1}{x}$.

3. Answer: $\csc(-\theta) = -\csc\theta$

Hint: Since $\csc\theta = \frac{1}{\sin\theta}$, the solution is similar to Example 1 except that $\csc\theta = \frac{1}{y}$.

4. Answer: $\cot(-\theta) = -\cot\theta$

Hint: Since $\cot\theta = \frac{1}{\tan\theta}$, the solution is similar to Problem 1 except that $\cot\theta = \frac{x}{y}$.

5. Answer: $\sin^2(-\theta) = \sin^2\theta$

Hints: One method is to realize that the square of any number is nonnegative. An alternative method is to write $\sin^2\theta = \sin\theta \sin\theta$ and use $\sin(-\theta) = -\sin\theta$. (Two minus signs multiplied will cancel out.)

6. Answer: $\cos^2(-\theta) = \cos^2\theta$

Hints: One method is to explain why an even function squared is even. An alternative method is to write $\cos^2\theta = \cos\theta \cos\theta$ and use $\cos(-\theta) = \cos\theta$.

7. Answer: $\sin^3(-\theta) = -\sin^3\theta$

Hints: Write $\sin^3\theta = \sin\theta \sin\theta \sin\theta$ and use $\sin(-\theta) = -\sin\theta$. (The product of three negative numbers is negative.)

8. Answer: $\cos^3(-\theta) = \cos^3\theta$

Hints: Write $\cos^3\theta = \cos\theta \cos\theta \cos\theta$ and use $\cos(-\theta) = \cos\theta$.

9. Answer: $\sin(-\theta)\cos(-\theta) = -\sin\theta \cos\theta$

Hints: Use $\sin(-\theta) = -\sin\theta$ and $\cos(-\theta) = \cos\theta$.

10. Answer: $\csc(-\theta)\cot(-\theta) = \csc\theta \cot\theta$

Hints: Use $\csc(-\theta) = -\csc\theta$ and $\cot(-\theta) = -\cot\theta$. See the solutions to Problems 3-4.

11. Answer: $\sin(-x) = -0.15$

Hint: $\sin(-\theta) = -\sin\theta$ so the sign of 0.15 changes; sine is odd.

12. Answer: $\cos(-x) = \frac{3}{4} = 0.75$

Hint: $\cos(-\theta) = \cos\theta$ so the sign of $\frac{3}{4}$ remains the same; cosine is even.

13. Answer: $\tan(-x) = -0.7$

Hint: $\tan(-\theta) = -\tan\theta$ so the sign of 0.7 changes; tangent is odd.

14. Answer: $\cot(-x) = -\frac{3}{2} = -1.5$

Hint: $\cot(-\theta) = -\cot\theta$ so the sign of $\frac{3}{2}$ changes; cotangent is odd.

15. Answer: $\sec(-x) = \frac{8}{5} = 1.6$

Hint: $\sec(-\theta) = \sec\theta$ so the sign of 1.6 remains the same; secant is even.

16. Answer: $\csc(-x) = \frac{5}{4} = 1.25$

Hint: $\csc(-\theta) = -\csc\theta$ so the sign of $-\frac{5}{4}$ changes; cosecant is odd.

Chapter 3 Angle Sum Formulas

1. Answer: $\sin(x \pm y) = \sin x \cos y \pm \sin y \cos x$

Hints: Begin with $\sin(x+y) = \frac{b+e}{d}$. All of the equations from Example 1 apply to this problem. Use those equations to substitute expressions into $\sin x \cos y + \sin y \cos x$; eliminate f and g by expressing these symbols in terms of a, b, c, d, and e. Note that $\frac{b^2}{c^2} + \frac{a^2}{c^2} = 1$ according to the Pythagorean theorem.

2. Answer: $\sec(x \pm y) = \frac{\sec x \sec y \csc x \csc y}{\csc x \csc y \mp \sec x \sec y}$

Hints: Begin with $\sec(x \pm y) = \frac{1}{\cos(x \pm y)}$. Apply the angle sum/difference formula for cosine. Divide the numerator and denominator each by $\cos x \cos y \sin x \sin y$.

3. Answer: $\csc(x \pm y) = \frac{\sec x \sec y \csc x \csc y}{\sec x \csc y \pm \csc x \sec y}$

Hints: Begin with $\csc(x \pm y) = \frac{1}{\sin(x \pm y)}$. Apply the angle sum/difference formula for sine. Divide the numerator and denominator each by $\cos x \cos y \sin x \sin y$.

4. Answer: $\cot(x \pm y) = \frac{\cot x \cot y \mp 1}{\cot y \pm \cot x}$

Hints: Begin with $\cot(x \pm y) = \frac{\cos(x \pm y)}{\sin(x \pm y)}$. Follow the strategy from Example 2.

5. Answer: $\sin 15° = \frac{\sqrt{6}-\sqrt{2}}{4}$

Hints: $\sin 15° = \sin(45° - 30°)$; apply the difference of angles formula for sine. Recall that $\sin 30° = \frac{1}{2}$, $\cos 30° = \frac{\sqrt{3}}{2}$, $\sin 45° = \frac{1}{\sqrt{2}} = \frac{\sqrt{2}}{2}$, and $\cos 45° = \frac{1}{\sqrt{2}} = \frac{\sqrt{2}}{2}$.

Calculator check: $\sin 15° \approx 0.2588$ and $\frac{\sqrt{6}-\sqrt{2}}{4} \approx 0.2588$

6. Answer: $\cos 15° = \frac{\sqrt{6}+\sqrt{2}}{4}$

Hints: $\cos 15° = \cos(45° - 30°)$; apply the difference of angles formula for cosine. Note that the formula for $\cos(x - y)$ adds the two terms, whereas $\cos(x + y)$ subtracts them.

Calculator check: $\cos 15° \approx 0.9659$ and $\frac{\sqrt{6}+\sqrt{2}}{4} \approx 0.9659$

7. Answer: $\tan 75° = 2 + \sqrt{3}$

Hints: $\tan 75° = \tan(45° + 30°)$; apply the sum of angles formula for tangent. Recall that $\tan 30° = \frac{1}{\sqrt{3}} = \frac{\sqrt{3}}{3}$ and $\tan 45° = 1$. Note that $\frac{1+\frac{1}{\sqrt{3}}}{1-\frac{1}{\sqrt{3}}} = \frac{\sqrt{3}+1}{\sqrt{3}-1}$ (multiply the numerator and denominator each by $\sqrt{3}$) and that $\frac{\sqrt{3}+1}{\sqrt{3}-1} = \frac{4+2\sqrt{3}}{2} = 2 + \sqrt{3}$ (multiply the numerator and denominator of $\frac{\sqrt{3}+1}{\sqrt{3}-1}$ each by $\sqrt{3} + 1$).

Calculator check: $\tan 75° \approx 3.732$ and $2 + \sqrt{3} \approx 3.732$

8. Answer: $\sec 105° = \frac{4}{\sqrt{2}-\sqrt{6}} = -\sqrt{2} - \sqrt{6}$ Note that this is a negative number; secant is negative in Quadrant II.

Hints: $\sec 105° = \sec(60° + 45°)$; apply the sum of angles formula for secant. Recall that $\sec 60° = 2$, $\csc 60° = \frac{2}{\sqrt{3}} = \frac{2\sqrt{3}}{3}$, $\sec 45° = \sqrt{2}$, and $\csc 45° = \sqrt{2}$. To rationalize the denominator of $\frac{4}{\sqrt{2}-\sqrt{6}}$, multiply the numerator and denominator each by the conjugate $(\sqrt{2} + \sqrt{6})$.

Calculator check: $\sec 105° \approx -3.864$ and $\frac{4}{\sqrt{2}-\sqrt{6}} = -\sqrt{2} - \sqrt{6} \approx -3.864$

9. Answer: $\csc 105° = \frac{4}{\sqrt{2}+\sqrt{6}} = \sqrt{6} - \sqrt{2}$

Hints: $\csc 105° = \csc(60° + 45°)$; apply the sum of angles formula for cosecant. To rationalize the denominator of $\frac{4}{\sqrt{2}+\sqrt{6}}$, multiply the numerator and denominator each by the conjugate $(\sqrt{6} - \sqrt{2})$.

Calculator check: $\csc 105° \approx 1.035$ and $\frac{4}{\sqrt{2}+\sqrt{6}} = \sqrt{6} - \sqrt{2} \approx 1.035$

10. Answer: $\cot 165° = \frac{1}{\sqrt{3}-2} = -\sqrt{3} - 2$ Note that this is a negative number; cotangent is negative in Quadrant II.

Hints: $\cot 165° = \cot(120° + 45°)$; apply the sum of angles formula for cotangent.

Recall that $\cot 120° = -\frac{1}{\sqrt{3}} = -\frac{\sqrt{3}}{3}$ and $\cot 45° = 1$. Note that $\frac{-\frac{1}{\sqrt{3}}-1}{1-\frac{1}{\sqrt{3}}} = \frac{-1-\sqrt{3}}{\sqrt{3}-1}$ and that

$\frac{-1-\sqrt{3}}{\sqrt{3}-1} = \frac{-4-2\sqrt{3}}{2} = -2 - \sqrt{3} = -\sqrt{3} - 2$ (see the hints for Problem 7).

Calculator check: $\cot 165° \approx -3.732$ and $\frac{1}{\sqrt{3}-2} = -\sqrt{3} - 2 \approx -3.732$

Chapter 4 Double Angle Formulas

1. Answer: $\sin(2x) = 2 \sin x \cos x$

Hint: Set $y = x$ in the sum of angles formula (Chapter 3) for sine.

2. Answer: $\tan(2x) = \frac{2 \tan x}{1-\tan^2 x}$

Hint: Set $y = x$ in the sum of angles formula (Chapter 3) for tangent.

3. Answer: $\cot(2x) = \frac{\cot^2 x - 1}{2 \cot x}$

Hint: Set $y = x$ in the sum of angles formula (Chapter 3) for cotangent.

4. Answer: $\cos(2x) = 2 \cos^2 x - 1$

Hints: Use the Pythagorean identity $\sin^2 x + \cos^2 x = 1$ from Chapter 1. Use this to eliminate $\sin^2 x$ from $\cos(2x) = \cos^2 x - \sin^2 x$. This is similar to Example 2, except that you will need to distribute a minus sign carefully.

5. Answer: $\csc(2x) = \frac{\sec x \csc x}{2}$

Hints: First write $\csc(2x) = \frac{1}{\sin(2x)}$. Now use the double angle formula for sine.

6. Answer: $\sec(2x) = \frac{\sec^2 x}{2-\sec^2 x}$

Hints: First write $\sec(2x) = \frac{1}{\cos(2x)}$. Now use the double angle formula from Problem 4. Divide the numerator and each term of the denominator by $\cos^2 x$.

7. Answer: $\sin(2x) = \frac{2 \tan x}{1+\tan^2 x}$

Hints: Begin with the double angle identity from Problem 1. Multiply by $\frac{\sec^2 x}{\sec^2 x}$ to get $\sin(2x) = \frac{2 \sin x \cos x \sec^2 x}{\sec^2 x}$. Show that the numerator simplifies to $2 \tan x$ and apply a Pythagorean identity (from Chapter 1) to the denominator.

8. Answer: $\cos(2x) = \frac{1-\tan^2 x}{1+\tan^2 x}$

Hints: Begin with the double angle identity from Example 1. Multiply by $\frac{\sec^2 x}{\sec^2 x}$ to get $\cos(2x) = \frac{\cos^2 x \sec^2 x - \sin^2 x \sec^2 x}{\sec^2 x}$. Show that the numerator simplifies to $1 - \tan^2 x$ and apply a Pythagorean identity (from Chapter 1) to the denominator.

9. Answers: $\frac{\pi}{12}$ or $\frac{5\pi}{12}$ rad (corresponding to $15°$ or $75°$)

Hints: Apply the double angle identity for sine. Isolate $\sin(2x)$. Take the inverse sine of both sides to find two possible answers for $2x$, and then divide each answer by 2 to solve for x. The answers for $2x$ lie in Quadrants I and II because $\sin(2x)$ is positive in Quadrants I and II (but after dividing by 2, the final answers for x lie in Quadrant I).

Check: $12 \sin\left(\frac{\pi}{12}\right)\cos\left(\frac{\pi}{12}\right) = 12\left(\frac{\sqrt{6}-\sqrt{2}}{4}\right)\left(\frac{\sqrt{6}+\sqrt{2}}{4}\right) = \frac{12}{16}(6-2) = \frac{3}{4}(4) = 3$ and

$12 \sin\left(\frac{5\pi}{12}\right)\cos\left(\frac{5\pi}{12}\right) = 12\left(\frac{\sqrt{6}+\sqrt{2}}{4}\right)\left(\frac{\sqrt{6}-\sqrt{2}}{4}\right) = \frac{12}{16}(6-2) = \frac{3}{4}(4) = 3$

Recall from Chapter 3 how to compute quantities like $\sin 15°$ without a calculator. (If you are not convinced, try entering $12 \sin\left(\frac{\pi}{12}\right)\cos\left(\frac{\pi}{12}\right)$ on a calculator if it is in radians mode or entering $12 \sin 15° \cos 15°$ on a calculator if it is in degrees mode.)

10. Answers: $\frac{\pi}{4}, \frac{3\pi}{4}, \frac{5\pi}{4}$ or $\frac{7\pi}{4}$ rad (corresponding to $45°$, $135°$, $225°$, or $315°$)

Hints: Use the double angle identity from Problem 4. Isolate $\cos^2 x$ and then square root both sides. Remember to include $\pm$ when you square root (for the same reasons that were discussed in Example 2 of Chapter 1). Take the inverse cosine of both sides. There is a $\pm$ when you square root both sides, and for each sign the inverse cosine has a solution in two different quadrants, giving a total of four possible answers.

Check: $2 \cos^2\left(\frac{\pi}{4}\right) + \cos\left[2\left(\frac{\pi}{4}\right)\right] = 2\left(\frac{1}{\sqrt{2}}\right)^2 + \cos\left(\frac{\pi}{2}\right) = 2\left(\frac{1}{2}\right) + 0 = 1$ and similarly for the other three answers.

11. Answers: $\frac{\pi}{12}$ or $\frac{7\pi}{12}$ rad (corresponding to $15°$ or $105°$)

Hints: Divide both sides by $1 - \tan^2 x$ and then divide both sides by $\sqrt{3}$. Now apply the double angle formula for tangent. Take the inverse tangent on both sides to find two possible answers for $2x$, and then divide each answer by 2 to solve for x. The answers for $2x$ lie in Quadrants I and III because $\tan(2x)$ is positive in Quadrants I and III (but after dividing by 2, the final answers for x lie in Quadrants I and II).

Check: $2\sqrt{3}\tan\left(\frac{\pi}{12}\right) = 2\sqrt{3}(2-\sqrt{3}) = 4\sqrt{3} - 2(3) = 4\sqrt{3} - 6$ agrees with

$1 - \tan^2\left(\frac{\pi}{12}\right) = 1 - (2-\sqrt{3})^2 = 1 - (4 - 4\sqrt{3} + 3) = 1 - (7 - 4\sqrt{3}) = 4\sqrt{3} - 6$

and $2\sqrt{3}\tan\left(\frac{7\pi}{12}\right) = 2\sqrt{3}(-2-\sqrt{3}) = -4\sqrt{3} - 2(3) = -4\sqrt{3} - 6$ agrees with

$1 - \tan^2\left(\frac{7\pi}{12}\right) = 1 - (-2-\sqrt{3})^2 = 1 - (4 + 4\sqrt{3} + 3) = 1 - (7 + 4\sqrt{3}) = -4\sqrt{3} - 6$

Recall from Chapter 3 how to compute quantities like $\tan 15°$ without a calculator. (If you are not convinced, try entering $2\sqrt{3}\tan\left(\frac{\pi}{12}\right)$ and $1 - \tan^2\left(\frac{\pi}{12}\right)$ on a calculator in radians mode or entering $2\sqrt{3}\tan 15°$ and $1 - \tan^2 15°$ in degrees mode.)

12. Answers: $\frac{\pi}{6}$ or $\frac{2\pi}{3}$ rad (corresponding to 30° or 120°)

Hints: Use the double angle identity for sine on the left. Factor out the $\sqrt{3}$ and apply the double angle identity for cosine from Example 1 on the right. Divide both sides of the equation by $\cos(2x)$. Take the inverse tangent on both sides to find two possible answers for $2x$, and then divide each answer by 2 to solve for x. The answers for $2x$ lie in Quadrants I and III because $\tan(2x)$ is positive in Quadrants I and III (but after dividing by 2, the final answers for x lie in Quadrants I and II).

Check: $2\sin\left(\frac{\pi}{6}\right)\cos\left(\frac{\pi}{6}\right) = 2\left(\frac{1}{2}\right)\left(\frac{\sqrt{3}}{2}\right) = \frac{\sqrt{3}}{2}$ agrees with

$\sqrt{3}\cos^2\left(\frac{\pi}{6}\right) - \sqrt{3}\sin^2\left(\frac{\pi}{6}\right) = \sqrt{3}\left(\frac{\sqrt{3}}{2}\right)^2 - \sqrt{3}\left(\frac{1}{2}\right)^2 = \sqrt{3}\left(\frac{3}{4}\right) - \sqrt{3}\left(\frac{1}{4}\right) = \sqrt{3}\left(\frac{1}{2}\right) = \frac{\sqrt{3}}{2}$

and $2\sin\left(\frac{2\pi}{3}\right)\cos\left(\frac{2\pi}{3}\right) = 2\left(\frac{\sqrt{3}}{2}\right)\left(-\frac{1}{2}\right) = -\frac{\sqrt{3}}{2}$ agrees with

$\sqrt{3}\cos^2\left(\frac{2\pi}{3}\right) - \sqrt{3}\sin^2\left(\frac{2\pi}{3}\right) = \sqrt{3}\left(\frac{1}{2}\right)^2 - \sqrt{3}\left(\frac{\sqrt{3}}{2}\right)^2 = \sqrt{3}\left(\frac{1}{4}\right) - \sqrt{3}\left(\frac{3}{4}\right) = \sqrt{3}\left(-\frac{1}{2}\right) = -\frac{\sqrt{3}}{2}$

13. Answers: $\frac{2\pi}{3}$ or $\frac{5\pi}{6}$ rad (corresponding to 120° or 150°)

Hints: Use $\sec x = \frac{1}{\cos x}$. Multiply both sides of the equation by $\cos x$. Use the double angle identity for sine. Isolate $\sin(2x)$. Take the inverse sine of both sides to find two possible answers for $2x$, and then divide each answer by 2 to solve for x. The answers for $2x$ lie in Quadrants III and IV because $\sin(2x)$ is negative in Quadrants III and IV (but after dividing by 2, the final answers for x lie in Quadrant II).

Check: $4\sin\left(\frac{2\pi}{3}\right) = 4\left(\frac{\sqrt{3}}{2}\right) = 2\sqrt{3}$ agrees with $-\sqrt{3}\sec\left(\frac{2\pi}{3}\right) = -\sqrt{3}(-2) = 2\sqrt{3}$

and $4\sin\left(\frac{5\pi}{6}\right) = 4\left(\frac{1}{2}\right) = 2$ agrees with $-\sqrt{3}\sec\left(\frac{5\pi}{6}\right) = -\sqrt{3}\left(-\frac{2}{\sqrt{3}}\right) = 2$

14. Answers: $\frac{\pi}{3}, \frac{2\pi}{3}, \frac{4\pi}{3}$, or $\frac{5\pi}{3}$ rad (corresponding to 60°, 120°, 240°, or 300°)

Hints: Use the double angle identity from Problem 4. Remember to distribute the 4. Combine like terms and isolate $\cos^2 x$. Square root both sides. Remember to include $\pm$ when you square root (for the same reasons that were discussed in Example 2 of Chapter 1). Take the inverse cosine of both sides. There is a $\pm$ when you square root both sides, and for each sign the inverse cosine has a solution in two different quadrants, giving a total of four possible answers.

Check: $4\cos^2\left(\frac{\pi}{3}\right) - 3 = 4\left(\frac{1}{2}\right)^2 - 3 = 4\left(\frac{1}{4}\right) - 3 = 1 - 3 = -2$ agrees with

$4\cos(2x) = 4\cos\left(\frac{2\pi}{3}\right) = 4\left(-\frac{1}{2}\right) = -2$,

$4\cos^2\left(\frac{2\pi}{3}\right) - 3 = 4\left(-\frac{1}{2}\right)^2 - 3 = 4\left(\frac{1}{4}\right) - 3 = 1 - 3 = -2$ agrees with

$4\cos(2x) = 4\cos\left(\frac{4\pi}{3}\right) = 4\left(-\frac{1}{2}\right) = -2$, and similarly for the other two answers.

15. Answers: $\frac{\pi}{2}, \frac{7\pi}{6}, \frac{3\pi}{2}$, or $\frac{11\pi}{6}$ rad (corresponding to 90°, 210°, 270°, or 330°)

Hints: Multiply both sides of the equation by $\cos(2x)$ to get $\sin(2x) = -\cos x$. Use the double angle identity for sine. Although it may be tempting to divide both sides by $\cos x$, to get all possible answers, instead add $\cos x$ to both sides and then factor out $\cos x$ to get $(2\sin x + 1)\cos x = 0$. Either $2\sin x + 1 = 0$ or $\cos x = 0$. Solve the two equations separately. The solutions to the first solution are $x = \frac{7\pi}{6}$ or $\frac{11\pi}{6}$ rad, while the solutions to $\cos x = 0$ are $x = \frac{\pi}{2}$ or $\frac{3\pi}{2}$ rad.

Check: $\tan(2x) = \tan\left[2\left(\frac{\pi}{2}\right)\right] = \tan\pi = 0$ agrees with

$-\sec\left[2\left(\frac{\pi}{2}\right)\right]\cos\left(\frac{\pi}{2}\right) = -\sec\pi\cos\left(\frac{\pi}{2}\right) = -(-1)(0) = 0$,

$\tan(2x) = \tan\left[2\left(\frac{7\pi}{6}\right)\right] = \tan\left(\frac{7\pi}{3}\right) = \sqrt{3}$ agrees with

$-\sec\left[2\left(\frac{7\pi}{6}\right)\right]\cos\left(\frac{7\pi}{6}\right) = -\sec\left(\frac{7\pi}{3}\right)\cos\left(\frac{7\pi}{6}\right) = -(2)\left(-\frac{\sqrt{3}}{2}\right) = \sqrt{3}$,

$\tan(2x) = \tan\left[2\left(\frac{3\pi}{2}\right)\right] = \tan(3\pi) = 0$ agrees with

$-\sec\left[2\left(\frac{3\pi}{2}\right)\right]\cos\left(\frac{3\pi}{2}\right) = -\sec(3\pi)\cos\left(\frac{\pi}{2}\right) = -(-1)(0) = 0$,

and $\tan(2x) = \tan\left[2\left(\frac{11\pi}{6}\right)\right] = \tan\left(\frac{11\pi}{3}\right) = -\sqrt{3}$ agrees with

$-\sec\left[2\left(\frac{11\pi}{6}\right)\right]\cos\left(\frac{11\pi}{6}\right) = -\sec\left(\frac{11\pi}{3}\right)\cos\left(\frac{11\pi}{6}\right) = -(2)\left(\frac{\sqrt{3}}{2}\right) = -\sqrt{3}$

16. Answer: $\frac{3\pi}{8}$ rad (corresponding to 67.5°)

Hints: Use $\csc(2x) = \frac{1}{\sin(2x)}$. Multiply both sides of the equation by $\sin(2x)$. Use the double angle identity for sine to relate $\sin(4x)$ to $\sin(2x)$. Note that $2\sin(2x)\cos(2x) = \sin(4x)$ because $4x$ is twice $2x$. Isolate $\sin(4x)$. Take the inverse sine of both sides to find the answer for $4x$, and then divide that answer by 4 to solve for x. Note that $\sin\left(\frac{3\pi}{2}\right) = \sin 270° = -1$. Another way to solve this problem is to first define $y = 2x$. Once you solve for y, then divide the answer for y by 2 in order to find x.

Check: $\csc\left[2\left(\frac{3\pi}{8}\right)\right] = \csc\left(\frac{3\pi}{4}\right) = \sqrt{2}$ agrees with

$-2\cos\left[2\left(\frac{3\pi}{8}\right)\right] = -2\cos\left(\frac{3\pi}{4}\right) = -2\left(-\frac{1}{\sqrt{2}}\right) = \sqrt{2}$

Chapter 5 Half-Angle Formulas

1. Answer: $\sin^2\left(\frac{x}{2}\right) = \frac{1-\cos x}{2}$

Hints: It may seem counterintuitive, but it is simplest to begin with the following double angle formula for **cosine** (even though you are deriving a half-angle formula for sine) from Chapter 4 written in terms of y (like Example 1): $\cos(2y) = 1 - 2\sin^2 y$. The reason for this is that this formula involves the sine of an angle and another trig function (the cosine) of twice the angle. Now isolate the $\sin^2 y$ (being careful with the minus signs). Finally, let $y = \frac{x}{2}$ such that $2y = x$.

2. Answer: $\cot^2\left(\frac{x}{2}\right) = \frac{1+\cos x}{1-\cos x}$

Hints: One method is to review Example 2. An alternative method is to use $\cot^2\left(\frac{x}{2}\right) = \frac{1}{\tan^2\left(\frac{x}{2}\right)}$ and the corresponding tangent half-angle formula.

3. Answer: $\tan\left(\frac{x}{2}\right) = \frac{\sin x}{1+\cos x}$

Hints: Begin with the tangent half-angle formula $\tan^2\left(\frac{x}{2}\right) = \frac{1-\cos x}{1+\cos x}$. On the right-hand side, multiply the numerator and denominator each by $1 + \cos x$ to get $\tan^2\left(\frac{x}{2}\right) = \frac{1-\cos^2 x}{(1+\cos x)^2}$. Use a Pythagorean identity from Chapter 1 and square root both sides. In the denominator, $\sqrt{(1 + \cos x)^2} = \pm(1 + \cos x)$. (The $\pm$ signs work themselves out.)

4. Answer: $\tan\left(\frac{x}{2}\right) = \frac{1-\cos x}{\sin x}$

Hints: Begin with the tangent half-angle formula $\tan^2\left(\frac{x}{2}\right) = \frac{1-\cos x}{1+\cos x}$. On the right-hand side, multiply the numerator and denominator each by $1 - \cos x$ to get $\tan^2\left(\frac{x}{2}\right) = \frac{(1-\cos x)^2}{1-\cos^2 x}$. Use a Pythagorean identity from Chapter 1 and square root both sides. In the numerator, $\sqrt{(1 - \cos x)^2} = \pm(1 - \cos x)$. (The $\pm$ signs work themselves out.)

5. Answer: $\tan\left(\frac{x}{2}\right) = \csc x - \cot x$

Hints: Use the answer to Problem 4. Recall the definitions of cosecant and cotangent.

6. Answer: $\cot\left(\frac{x}{2}\right) = \csc x + \cot x$

Hints: Use the answer to Problem 3. Take the reciprocal of both sides, noting that $\cot\left(\frac{x}{2}\right) = \frac{1}{\tan\left(\frac{x}{2}\right)}$. Recall the definitions of cosecant and cotangent. (If you attempt to take the reciprocal of both sides of the answer to Problem 5 instead of Problem 3, note that you will get a single fraction with $\csc x + \cot x$ in the denominator and not two separate fractions. A fraction of the form $\frac{a+b}{c} = \frac{a}{c} + \frac{b}{c}$ can be split into two fractions, but a fraction of the form $\frac{d}{e+f}$ does not split similarly.)

7. Answer: $\cot\left(\frac{x}{2}\right) = \frac{1+\sec x}{\tan x}$

Hints: Use the answer to Problem 3. Divide the numerator and denominator each by $\cos x$ to get $\tan\left(\frac{x}{2}\right) = \frac{\tan x}{\sec x+1}$. Now take the reciprocal of both sides.

8. Answer: $\tan\left(\frac{x}{2}\right) = \frac{-1\pm\sqrt{1+\tan^2 x}}{\tan x}$

Hints: Use the answer to Problem 4. Divide the numerator and denominator each by $\cos x$ to get $\tan\left(\frac{x}{2}\right) = \frac{\sec x-1}{\tan x} = \frac{-1+\sec x}{\tan x}$. Use a Pythagorean identity from Chapter 1 to write $\sec x = \pm\sqrt{1 + \tan^2 x}$.

9. Answer: $\sec^2\left(\frac{x}{2}\right) = \frac{2}{1+\cos x}$

Hints: Recall the definition of secant. Use the answer to Example 1.

10. Answer: $\csc^2\left(\frac{x}{2}\right) = \frac{2}{1-\cos x}$

Hints: Recall the definition of cosecant. Use the answer to Problem 1.

11. Answer: $\sqrt{\dfrac{1}{2} - \dfrac{\sqrt{3}}{4}} = \sqrt{\dfrac{2-\sqrt{3}}{4}} = \dfrac{\sqrt{2-\sqrt{3}}}{2} = \sqrt{\dfrac{\frac{3}{2}-\sqrt{3}+\frac{1}{2}}{2}} = \sqrt{\dfrac{\frac{6-4\sqrt{3}+2}{4}}{2}} = \dfrac{\frac{\sqrt{6}}{2}-\frac{\sqrt{2}}{2}}{2} = \dfrac{\sqrt{6}-\sqrt{2}}{4}$

Note: We applied a little algebra to tidy up the expression, since a radical inside of a radical is not the most desirable form for an answer. The main idea is this:

$$\left(\sqrt{6} - \sqrt{2}\right)^2 = 6 - 2\sqrt{12} + 2 = 8 - 2\sqrt{12} = 8 - 4\sqrt{3}$$

It follows that $\sqrt{6} - \sqrt{2} = \sqrt{8 - 4\sqrt{3}}$, which means that

$$\dfrac{\sqrt{6} - \sqrt{2}}{4} = \dfrac{\sqrt{8 - 4\sqrt{3}}}{4} = \sqrt{\dfrac{8}{4^2} - \dfrac{4\sqrt{3}}{4^2}} = \sqrt{\dfrac{1}{2} - \dfrac{\sqrt{3}}{4}}$$

We effectively did this in reverse at the top of this page:

$$\sqrt{\dfrac{1}{2} - \dfrac{\sqrt{3}}{4}} = \sqrt{\dfrac{8}{4^2} - \dfrac{4\sqrt{3}}{4^2}} = \dfrac{\sqrt{8 - 4\sqrt{3}}}{4} = \dfrac{\sqrt{6} - \sqrt{2}}{4}$$

Use a calculator if needed to help see which quantities are numerically equivalent. For example, $\dfrac{\sqrt{2-\sqrt{3}}}{2} \approx 0.2588$ and $\dfrac{\sqrt{6}-\sqrt{2}}{4} \approx 0.2588$.

Hint: Use the half-angle formula for sine with $x = 30°$. When you square root both sides, keep the positive root since the sine function is positive in Quadrant I.

Calculator check: $\sin 15° \approx 0.2588$ and $\dfrac{\sqrt{6}-\sqrt{2}}{4} \approx 0.2588$

12. Answer: $\sqrt{\dfrac{1}{2} + \dfrac{\sqrt{3}}{4}} = \sqrt{\dfrac{2+\sqrt{3}}{4}} = \dfrac{\sqrt{2+\sqrt{3}}}{2} = \sqrt{\dfrac{\frac{3}{2}+\sqrt{3}+\frac{1}{2}}{2}} = \sqrt{\dfrac{\frac{6+4\sqrt{3}+2}{4}}{2}} = \dfrac{\frac{\sqrt{6}}{2}+\frac{\sqrt{2}}{2}}{2} = \dfrac{\sqrt{6}+\sqrt{2}}{4}$

See the notes following the answer to Problem 11.

Hints: Use the half-angle formula for cosine with $x = 30°$. When you square root both sides, keep the positive root since the cosine function is positive in Quadrant I.

Note: An alternative method is to use the Answer to Problem 11 and a Pythagorean identity from Chapter 1. (If the instructions did not explicitly state to use a half-angle formula, you could also use a difference of angle formula from Chapter 3.)

Calculator check: $\cos 15° \approx 0.9659$ and $\dfrac{\sqrt{6}+\sqrt{2}}{4} \approx 0.9659$

13. Answer: $2 + \sqrt{3}$

Hints: Use one of the half-angle formulas for tangent, such as $\tan\left(\dfrac{x}{2}\right) = \csc x - \cot x$, with $x = 150°$. Note that subtracting a negative number equates to addition.

Calculator check: $\tan 75° \approx 3.732$ and $2 + \sqrt{3} \approx 3.732$

14. Answer: $-\sqrt{\dfrac{1}{2}-\dfrac{\sqrt{3}}{4}} = -\sqrt{\dfrac{2-\sqrt{3}}{4}} = -\dfrac{\sqrt{2-\sqrt{3}}}{2} = -\dfrac{\sqrt{\frac{3}{2}-\sqrt{3}+\frac{1}{2}}}{2} = -\dfrac{\sqrt{\frac{6-4\sqrt{3}+2}{4}}}{2} = \dfrac{\frac{\sqrt{2}}{2}-\frac{\sqrt{6}}{2}}{2} = \dfrac{\sqrt{2}-\sqrt{6}}{4}$

See the notes following the answer to Problem 11. There is an overall minus sign here because cosine is negative in Quadrant II; we have $\sqrt{2}-\sqrt{6}$ instead of $\sqrt{6}-\sqrt{2}$.

Hints: Use the half-angle formula for cosine with $x = 210°$. When you square root both sides, keep the negative root since the cosine function is negative in Quadrant II. (Since you are solving for $\cos 105°$, the answer lies in Quadrant II. In contrast, when you compute $\cos 210°$ during the solution, that angle lies in Quadrant III.)

Calculator check: $\cos 105° \approx -0.2588$ and $\dfrac{\sqrt{2}-\sqrt{6}}{4} \approx -0.2588$

15. Answer: $\sqrt{\dfrac{1}{2}-\dfrac{\sqrt{3}}{4}} = \sqrt{\dfrac{2-\sqrt{3}}{4}} = \dfrac{\sqrt{2-\sqrt{3}}}{2} = \dfrac{\sqrt{\frac{3}{2}-\sqrt{3}+\frac{1}{2}}}{2} = \dfrac{\sqrt{\frac{6-4\sqrt{3}+2}{4}}}{2} = \dfrac{\frac{\sqrt{6}}{2}-\frac{\sqrt{2}}{2}}{2} = \dfrac{\sqrt{6}-\sqrt{2}}{4}$

See the notes following the answer to Problem 11.

Hints: Use the half-angle formula for sine with $x = 330°$. When you square root both sides, keep the positive root since the sine function is positive in Quadrant II. (Since you are solving for $\sin 165°$, the answer lies in Quadrant II. In contrast, when you compute $\cos 330°$ during the solution, that angle lies in Quadrant IV.)

Calculator check: $\sin 165° \approx 0.2588$ and $\dfrac{\sqrt{6}-\sqrt{2}}{4} \approx 0.2588$

16. Answer: $\dfrac{2}{\sqrt{2-\sqrt{2}}} = \dfrac{2\sqrt{2+\sqrt{2}}}{\sqrt{2-\sqrt{2}}\sqrt{2+\sqrt{2}}} = \dfrac{2\sqrt{2+\sqrt{2}}}{\sqrt{4-2}} = \dfrac{2\sqrt{2+\sqrt{2}}}{\sqrt{2}} = \sqrt{2}\sqrt{2+\sqrt{2}} = \sqrt{4+2\sqrt{2}}$

Side note: Unlike the answers to Problems 11-12 and 14-15, $\sqrt{4+2\sqrt{2}}$ can not have the nested square roots removed using only real numbers. If you attempt to do it, you will need to use complex numbers like this (where $2^{1/4}$ is the fourth root of two):

$$\sqrt{4+2\sqrt{2}} = 2^{1/4}\sqrt{1+i} + 2^{1/4}\sqrt{1-i}$$

Here is a quick check:

$$\left(2^{1/4}\sqrt{1+i} + 2^{1/4}\sqrt{1-i}\right)^2 = \sqrt{2}\left(1+i+1-i+2\sqrt{2}\right) = \sqrt{2}\left(2+2\sqrt{2}\right) = 2\sqrt{2}+4$$

Since complex numbers are beyond the scope of this book, we will accept $\sqrt{4+2\sqrt{2}}$.

Note that we rationalized the denominator of $\dfrac{2}{\sqrt{2-\sqrt{2}}}$ to transform it into $\sqrt{4+2\sqrt{2}}$.

Hints: Use the half-angle formula for secant with $x = 135°$. When you square root both sides, keep the positive root since the secant function is positive in Quadrant I.

(Since you are solving for sec 67.5°, the answer lies in Quadrant I. In contrast, when you compute cos 135° during the solution, that angle lies in Quadrant II.)

Calculator check: $\sec 67.5° \approx 2.613$ and $\sqrt{4 + 2\sqrt{2}} \approx 2.613$

17. Answer: $\dfrac{2}{\sqrt{2+\sqrt{2}}} = \dfrac{2\sqrt{2-\sqrt{2}}}{\sqrt{2+\sqrt{2}}\sqrt{2-\sqrt{2}}} = \dfrac{2\sqrt{2-\sqrt{2}}}{\sqrt{4-2}} = \dfrac{2\sqrt{2-\sqrt{2}}}{\sqrt{2}} = \sqrt{2}\sqrt{2 - \sqrt{2}} = \sqrt{4 - 2\sqrt{2}}$

See the side note following the answer to Problem 16.

Hints: Use the half-angle formula for cosecant with $x = 225°$. When you square root both sides, keep the positive root since the cosecant function is positive in Quadrant II. (Since you are solving for csc 112.5°, the answer lies in Quadrant II. In contrast, when you compute cos 225° during the solution, that angle lies in Quadrant III.) Note that subtracting a negative number equates to addition.

Calculator check: $\csc 112.5° \approx 1.082$ and $\sqrt{4 - 2\sqrt{2}} \approx 1.082$

18. Answer: $-1 - \sqrt{2}$

Hint: Use one of the half-angle formulas for cotangent, such as $\cot\left(\dfrac{x}{2}\right) = \csc x + \cot x$, with $x = 315°$.

Calculator check: $\cot 157.5° \approx -2.414$ and $-1 - \sqrt{2} \approx -2.414$

19. Answer: $\sqrt{\dfrac{1}{2} - \dfrac{\sqrt{6}+\sqrt{2}}{8}} = \dfrac{\sqrt{8-2\sqrt{6}-2\sqrt{2}}}{4}$ Alternate answer: $\dfrac{\sqrt{2-\sqrt{2+\sqrt{3}}}}{2}$

Notes: $\dfrac{\sqrt{8-2\sqrt{6}-2\sqrt{2}}}{4}$ is the preferred form, as it has minimal nesting of radicals and the

denominator is rational. The form $\dfrac{\sqrt{2-\sqrt{2+\sqrt{3}}}}{2}$, which is relatively common, arises when the student does not remove the nested radicals for cos 15° (see the notes following the solutions to Problem 11 and the answer to Problem 12).

Hints: Use the half-angle formula for sine with $x = 15°$ with the answer to Problem 12 for cos 15°. When you square root both sides, keep the positive root since the sine function is positive in Quadrant I.

Calculator check: $\sin 7.5° \approx 0.1305$ and $\dfrac{\sqrt{8-2\sqrt{6}-2\sqrt{2}}}{4} \approx 0.1305$

20. Answer: $\dfrac{\sqrt{2+\sqrt{2+\sqrt{2}}}}{2}$

Hints: First find $\cos 22.5° = \dfrac{\sqrt{2+\sqrt{2}}}{2}$, using the half-angle formula for cosine with $x = 45°$. Then use the half-angle formula for cosine a second time, now with $x = 22.5°$.

Calculator check: $\cos 11.25° \approx 0.9808$ and $\dfrac{\sqrt{2+\sqrt{2+\sqrt{2}}}}{2} \approx 0.9808$

Chapter 6 Triple Angle Formulas

1. Answer: $\sin(3x) = 3\sin x - 4\sin^3 x$

Hints: Set $y = 2x$ in the sum of angles formula (Chapter 3) for sine. Apply the double angle formulas (Chapter 4) for cosine and sine, like we did in Example 1. Apply one of the Pythagorean identities (Chapter 1), like we did in Example 1.

2. Answer: $\tan(3x) = \dfrac{3\tan x - \tan^3 x}{1 - 3\tan^2 x}$

Hints: Set $y = 2x$ in the sum of angles formula (Chapter 3) for tangent. Apply the double angle formula (Chapter 4) for tangent. Multiply each term of the numerator and the denominator by $1 - \tan^2 x$.

3. Answer: $\cot(3x) = \dfrac{3\cot x - \cot^3 x}{1 - 3\cot^2 x}$

Hints: Set $y = 2x$ in the sum of angles formula (Chapter 3) for cotangent. Apply the double angle formula (Chapter 4) for cotangent. Multiply each term of the numerator and the denominator by $2\cot x$. Multiply each term of the numerator and denominator by -1.

4. Answer: $\sec(3x) = \dfrac{\sec^3 x}{4 - 3\sec^2 x}$

Hints: Long method: Set $y = 2x$ in the sum of angles formula (Chapter 3) for secant. Apply the double angle formulas (Chapter 4) for secant and cosecant. Multiply each term of the numerator and denominator by 2; this will cancel a 2 in the numerator and one 2 from the denominator, while the second term in the denominator will get a coefficient of 2. Also multiply each term of the numerator and denominator by $2 - \sec^2 x$. After you distribute and simplify, you should have

$$\sec(3x) = \frac{\sec^4 x \csc^2 x}{2\csc^2 x \sec x - \csc^2 x \sec^3 x - 2\sec^3 x}$$

Divide each term of the numerator and denominator by $\sec x$. Divide each term of the numerator and denominator by $\csc^2 x$. Note that $\dfrac{\sec^2 x}{\csc^2 x} = \tan^2 x$. You should now have

$$\sec(3x) = \frac{\sec^3 x}{2 - \sec^2 x - 2\tan^2 x}$$

Apply the Pythagorean identity $\tan^2 x + 1 = \sec^2 x$ from Chapter 1. Rewrite this as $2\tan^2 x = 2\sec^2 x - 2$. Be careful with the signs when you distribute. If you do this correctly, the denominator will become $4 - 3\sec^2 x$.

Short method: Start with $\dfrac{1}{\cos(3x)}$. Divide the numerator and denominator by $\cos^3 x$.

5. Answer: $\csc(3x) = \dfrac{\csc^3 x}{3\csc^2 x - 4}$

Hints: Long method: Set $y = 2x$ in the sum of angles formula (Chapter 3) for cosecant. Apply the double angle formulas (Chapter 4) for secant and cosecant. Multiply each term of the numerator and denominator by 2; this will cancel a 2 in the numerator and one 2 from the denominator, while the second term in the denominator will get a coefficient of 2. Also multiply each term of the numerator and denominator by $2 - \sec^2 x$. After you distribute and simplify, you should have

$$\frac{\sec^4 x \csc^2 x}{4\sec^2 x \csc x - \sec^4 x \csc x}$$

Divide each term of the numerator and denominator by $\sec^4 x$. Multiply each term of the numerator and denominator by $\csc x$. Note that $\dfrac{\csc^2 x}{\sec^2 x} = \cot^2 x$. You should now have

$$\frac{\csc^3 x}{4\cot^2 x - \csc^2 x}$$

Apply the Pythagorean identity $1 + \cot^2 x = \csc^2 x$ from Chapter 1. Rewrite this as $4\cot^2 x = 4\csc^2 x - 4$. The denominator will become $3\csc^2 x - 4$.

Short method: Start with $\dfrac{1}{\sin(3x)}$. Divide the numerator and denominator by $\sin^3 x$.

Chapter 7 Power Reduction Formulas

1. Answer: $\sin^2 x = \dfrac{1 - \cos(2x)}{2}$

Hints: Although this is an identity for $\sin^2 x$, you do not want to use the double angle formula for sine because that identity does not have $\sin^2 x$. Instead, it makes sense to use the following double angle formula (Chapter 4) for cosine: $\cos(2x) = 1 - 2\sin^2 x$. Isolate $\sin^2 x$. An alternative method is to write the half-angle formula for sine in terms of y: $\sin^2\left(\dfrac{y}{2}\right) = \dfrac{1 - \cos y}{2}$. Then write $\dfrac{y}{2} = x$ such that $y = 2x$.

2. Answer: $\sin^3 x = \dfrac{3\sin x - \sin(3x)}{4}$

Hints: Use the triple angle formula (Chapter 6) for sine. Isolate $\sin^3 x$.

3. Answer: $\sin^4 x = \dfrac{3 - 4\cos(2x) + \cos(4x)}{8}$

Hints: Square both sides of the formula from Problem 1. In the numerator, you should get $1 - 2\cos(2x) + \cos^2(2x)$. Write the power reduction formula for $\cos^2 x$ in terms of y: $\cos^2 y = \dfrac{1 + \cos(2y)}{2}$. Let $y = 2x$ to get $\cos^2(2x) = \dfrac{1 + \cos(4x)}{2}$. Substitute this into the previous equation. Add the three quantities in the numerator by finding a common denominator: $1 - 2\cos(2x) = \frac{2 - 4\cos(2x)}{2}$. Combine like terms. Think of the nested fraction as having the form $\frac{\frac{a}{2}}{\frac{4}{1}}$. Recall that the way to divide fractions is to multiply by the reciprocal of the second fraction: $\frac{\frac{a}{2}}{\frac{4}{1}} = \frac{a}{2}\frac{1}{4} = \frac{a}{8}$.

4. Answer: $\cos^4 x = \frac{3 + 4\cos(2x) + \cos(4x)}{8}$

Hints: Square both sides of the formula from Example 1. In the numerator, you should get $1 + 2\cos(2x) + \cos^2(2x)$. See the hints for the solution to Problem 3.

5. Answer: $\sin(5x) = 16\sin^5 x - 10\sin x + 5\sin(3x)$

Hints: Begin with the sum of angles formula (Chapter 3) for sine, using $3x$ and $2x$ for the two angles. Use the triple angle formulas (Chapter 6); plug these expressions into the equation from the sum of angles formula. After you distribute, you should have

$$\sin(5x) = 3\sin x \cos(2x) - 4\sin^3 x \cos(2x) + 4\cos^3 x \sin(2x) - 3\cos x \sin(2x)$$

Use the double angle formula (Chapter 4) for sine and this double angle formula for cosine: $\cos(2x) = 1 - 2\sin^2 x$. After you distribute, you should have

$$\sin(5x) = 3\sin x - 6\sin^3 x - 4\sin^3 x + 8\sin^5 x + 8\cos^4 x \sin x - 6\cos^2 x \sin x$$

Use the Pythagorean identity (Chapter 1) $\cos^2 x = 1 - \sin^2 x$. Also, square both sides of this identity to get an expression for $\cos^4 x$. After you simplify, you should have

$$\sin(5x) = 16\sin^5 x - 20\sin^3 x + 5\sin x$$

Now use the power reduction formula from Problem 2.

$$\sin(5x) = 16\sin^5 x - 20\frac{3\sin x - \sin(3x)}{4} + 5\sin x$$

6. Answer: $\sin^5 x = \frac{10\sin x - 5\sin(3x) + \sin(5x)}{16}$

Hints: Use the formula from Problem 5. Isolate $\sin^5 x$.

7. Answer: $\cos(5x) = 16\cos^5 x - 10\cos x - 5\cos(3x)$

Hints: Begin with the sum of angles formula (Chapter 3) for cosine, using $3x$ and $2x$ for the two angles. Use the triple angle formulas (Chapter 6); plug these expressions into the equation from the sum of angles formula. After you distribute, you should have

$$\cos(5x) = 4\cos^3 x \cos(2x) - 3\cos x \cos(2x) - 3\sin x \sin(2x) + 4\sin^3 x \sin(2x)$$

Use the double angle formula (Chapter 4) for sine and this double angle formula for cosine: $\cos(2x) = 2\cos^2 x - 1$. After you distribute, you should have

$$\cos(5x) = 8\cos^5 x - 10\cos^3 x + 3\cos x - 6\sin^2 x \cos x + 8\sin^4 x \cos x$$

Use the Pythagorean identity (Chapter 1) $\sin^2 x = 1 - \cos^2 x$. Also, square both sides of this identity to get an expression for $\sin^4 x$. After you simplify, you should have

$$\cos(5x) = 16\cos^5 x - 20\cos^3 x + 5\cos x$$

Now use the power reduction formula from Example 2.

$$\cos(5x) = 16\cos^5 x - 20\,\frac{3\cos x + \cos(3x)}{4} + 5\cos x$$

8. Answer: $\cos^5 x = \frac{10\cos x + 5\cos(3x) + \cos(5x)}{16}$

Hints: Use the formula from Problem 7. Isolate $\cos^5 x$.

9. Answer: $\tan^2 x = 1 - 2\,\frac{\tan x}{\tan(2x)}$

Hints: Use the double angle formula (Chapter 4) for tangent. Isolate $\tan^2 x$.

10. Answer: $\cot^2 x = 2\cot(2x)\cot x + 1$

Hints: Use the double angle formula (Chapter 4) for cotangent. Isolate $\cot^2 x$.

11. Answer: $\tan^3 x = 3\tan x + 2\tan(3x) - 6\,\frac{\tan x \tan(3x)}{\tan(2x)}$

Hints: Use the triple angle formula (Chapter 6) for tangent. Isolate $\tan^3 x$. Eliminate $\tan^2 x$ using the answer to Problem 9.

12. Answer: $\cot^3 x = 3\cot x + 2\cot(3x) + 6\cot x \cot(2x)\cot(3x)$

Hints: Use the triple angle formula (Chapter 6) for cotangent. Isolate $\cot^3 x$. Eliminate $\cot^2 x$ using the answer to Problem 10.

13. Answer: $\sec^2 x = \frac{2\sec(2x)}{\sec(2x)+1}$

Hints: Use the double angle formula (Chapter 4) for secant. Isolate $\sec^2 x$. First, multiply both sides of the equation by $2 - \sec^2 x$ and distribute. Next, combine like terms. Add $\sec^2 x \sec(2x)$ to both sides, then factor out the $\sec^2 x$. Alternatively, see the hints to 14.

14. Answer: $\csc^2 x = \frac{2\sec(2x)}{\sec(2x)-1}$

Hints: Although this is an identity for $\csc^2 x$, you do not want to use the double angle formula for cosecant because that identity does not have $\csc^2 x$. A more direct route is to begin with the answer to Problem 1 and take the reciprocal of both sides, noting that $\csc^2 x = \frac{1}{\sin^2 x}$. Next divide the numerator and each term of the denominator by $\cos(2x)$, noting that $\frac{1}{\cos(2x)} = \sec(2x)$.

15. Answer: $\sec^3 x = 4\sec(3x) - 6\,\frac{\sec(2x)\sec(3x)}{\sec(2x)+1}$

Hints: Use the triple angle formula (Chapter 6) for secant. Isolate $\sec^3 x$. Eliminate $\sec^2 x$ using the answer to Problem 13.

16. Answer: $\csc^3 x = -4\csc(3x) + 6\frac{\sec(2x)\csc(3x)}{\sec(2x)-1}$

Hints: Use the triple angle formula (Chapter 6) for cosecant. Isolate $\csc^3 x$. Eliminate $\csc^2 x$ using the answer to Problem 14.

Chapter 8 Sum/Product Formulas

1. Answer: $\cos x \cos y = \frac{\cos(x-y)+\cos(x+y)}{2}$

Hint: Follow Example 1.

2. Answer: $\sin x \cos y = \frac{\sin(x+y)+\sin(x-y)}{2}$

Hint: Follow Example 1.

3. Answer: $\cos x \sin y = \frac{\sin(x+y)-\sin(x-y)}{2}$

Hint: Follow Example 1.

4. Answer: $\tan x \tan y = \frac{\cos(x-y)-\cos(x+y)}{\cos(x-y)+\cos(x+y)}$

Hints: Recall that $\tan x = \frac{\sin x}{\cos x}$. Substitute the answers to Example 1 and Problem 1 into the numerator and denominator.

5. Answer: $\sec^2 x + \csc^2 x = \sec^2 x \csc^2 x$

Hints: Begin with the Pythagorean identity (Chapter 1) $\sin^2 x + \cos^2 x = 1$. Divide by $\sin^2 x \cos^2 x$ on each side of the equation. Recall the definitions of secant and cosecant.

6. Answer: $\sin x - \sin y = 2\sin\left(\frac{x-y}{2}\right)\cos\left(\frac{x+y}{2}\right)$

Hint: Follow Example 2.

7. Answer: $\cos x + \cos y = 2\cos\left(\frac{x+y}{2}\right)\cos\left(\frac{x-y}{2}\right)$

Hint: Follow Example 2.

8. Answer: $\cos x - \cos y = -2\sin\left(\frac{x+y}{2}\right)\sin\left(\frac{x-y}{2}\right)$

Hint: Follow Example 2.

Chapter 9 Angle Shifting Identities

1. Answer: $\sin(x+\pi) = -\sin x$

Hints: Use the sum of angles formula. Recall that $\sin\pi = 0$ and $\cos\pi = -1$.

2. Answer: $\cos(x + \pi) = -\cos x$
Hints: Use the sum of angles formula. Recall that $\sin \pi = 0$ and $\cos \pi = -1$.
3. Answer: $\csc(x + \pi) = -\csc x$
Hints: Use $\csc(x + \pi) = \frac{1}{\sin(x+\pi)}$. (This avoids the domain problem with $\csc \pi$.)
4. Answer: $\sec(x + \pi) = -\sec x$
Hints: Use $\sec(x + \pi) = \frac{1}{\cos(x+\pi)}$. (This avoids the domain problem with $\csc \pi$.)
5. Answer: $\tan(x + \pi) = \tan x$
Hints: Use the sum of angles formula. Alternatively, note that $\tan(x + \pi) = \frac{\sin(x+\pi)}{\cos(x+\pi)}$.
6. Answer: $\cot(x + \pi) = \cot x$
Hints: Use $\cot(x + \pi) = \frac{1}{\tan(x+\pi)}$. (This avoids the domain problem with $\cot \pi$.)
7. Answer: $\sin\left(x \pm \frac{\pi}{2}\right) = \pm \cos x$
Hints: Use the angle sum/difference formula. Recall that $\sin\left(\frac{\pi}{2}\right) = 1$ and $\cos\left(\frac{\pi}{2}\right) = 0$.
8. Answer: $\cos\left(x \pm \frac{\pi}{2}\right) = \mp \sin x$
Hints: Use the angle sum/difference formula. Recall that $\sin\left(\frac{\pi}{2}\right) = 1$ and $\cos\left(\frac{\pi}{2}\right) = 0$.
Note that $\cos\left(x \pm \frac{\pi}{2}\right) = \mp \sin x$ means $\cos\left(x + \frac{\pi}{2}\right) = -\sin x$ and $\cos\left(x - \frac{\pi}{2}\right) = \sin x$.
9. Answer: $\tan\left(x + \frac{\pi}{2}\right) = -\cot x$
Hints: Use $\tan\left(x + \frac{\pi}{2}\right) = \frac{\sin\left(x+\frac{\pi}{2}\right)}{\cos\left(x+\frac{\pi}{2}\right)}$. (This avoids the domain problem with $\tan\frac{\pi}{2}$.)
10. Answer: $\sin(\pi - x) = \sin x$
Hints: Use the difference of angles formula. Recall that $\sin \pi = 0$ and $\cos \pi = -1$.
11. Answer: $\cos(\pi - x) = -\cos x$
Hints: Use the difference of angles formula. Recall that $\sin \pi = 0$ and $\cos \pi = -1$.
12. Answer: $\tan(\pi - x) = -\tan x$
Hints: Use the difference of angles formula. Alternatively, note that $\tan(\pi - x) = \frac{\sin(\pi-x)}{\cos(\pi-x)}$.
13. Answer: $\cos\left(\frac{\pi}{2} - x\right) = \sin x$
Hints: Use the difference of angles formula. Recall that $\sin\left(\frac{\pi}{2}\right) = 1$ and $\cos\left(\frac{\pi}{2}\right) = 0$.
14. Answer: $\tan\left(\frac{\pi}{2} - x\right) = \cot x$
Hints: Use $\tan\left(\frac{\pi}{2} - x\right) = \frac{\sin\left(\frac{\pi}{2}-x\right)}{\cos\left(\frac{\pi}{2}-x\right)}$. (This avoids the domain problem with $\tan\frac{\pi}{2}$.)

15. Answer: Show that $\cos(-x) = \cos x$.

Hint: Review Example 2.

16. Answer: Show that $\tan(-x) = -\tan x$.

Hint: Review Example 2.

Chapter 10 Law of Sines

1. Answer: $\dfrac{\sin A}{a} = \dfrac{\sin B}{b}$

Hints: Think of side c as the base (turn the book around so that c appears to be the "bottom" side) and draw the height of the triangle from this perspective, as shown below. Write equations for $\sin A$ and $\sin B$ in the two small right triangles. You should get $\sin A = \dfrac{h}{b}$ and $\sin B = \dfrac{h}{a}$. Complete the solution like we did in Example 1.

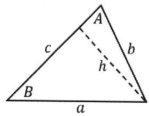

2. Answer: $\dfrac{\sin A}{a} = \dfrac{\sin C}{c}$

Hints: Think of side b as the base (turn the book around so that b appears to be the "bottom" side) and draw the height of the triangle from this perspective, as shown below. Write equations for $\sin A$ and $\sin C$ in the two small right triangles. You should get $\sin A = \dfrac{h}{c}$ and $\sin C = \dfrac{h}{a}$. Complete the solution like we did in Example 1.

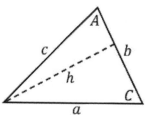

3. Answer: $\dfrac{\sin B}{b} = \dfrac{\sin C}{c}$

Hints: The solution is similar to the solution of Example 1. One difference is that the height "looks" different (see the next page). Another difference is that you need to use $\sin B$ and $\sin H$, and then use $H = \pi - C$. Recall from Chapter 9 that $\sin(\pi - x) = \sin x$.

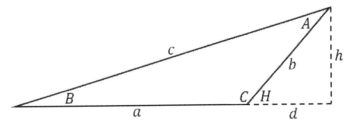

4. Answer: $\frac{\sin A}{a} = \frac{\sin B}{b} = \frac{\sin C}{c} = \frac{1}{d}$

Hints: We have already shown that the law of sines is true. For this problem, you just need to show that one of the ratios is equal to the reciprocal of the diameter of the circle. To do this, draw a line to connect the other end of the diameter to one of the other two vertices. See side e in the left diagram below. Consider two triangles: one triangle has sides a, b, and c, while the other triangle has sides b, d, and e. Note that in each triangle, one of the angles is B. This follows from the inscribed angle theorem of geometry. According to the **inscribed angle theorem**, if two angles inscribed in the same circle intercept the same arc length, the two angles are congruent; the angles in question each intercept the arc length defined by the endpoints of side b. Also note that the triangle with sides b, d, and e (shown on the right) is a right triangle according to Thales's theorem. According to **Thales's theorem**, if a triangle is inscribed in a circle such that one side of the triangle is a diameter of the circle, the angle opposite to the diameter is a right angle. Find the sine of B in the triangle on the right. You should get $\sin B = \frac{b}{d}$. Divide both sides of this equation by b to get $\frac{\sin B}{b} = \frac{1}{d}$.

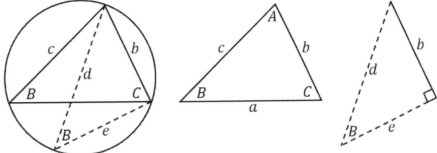

5. Answer: $6\sqrt{2}$

Hints: Note that 6 is opposite to 30°. Call these $a = 6$ and $A = 30°$. Call the other angle $B = 45°$. The left side is its opposite, so call this b. Use the formula $\frac{\sin A}{a} = \frac{\sin B}{b}$.

6. Answer: 45° (note that 135° would not work since the 3 angles must add up to 180°)

Hints: Note that $\sqrt{6}$ is opposite to 120°. Call these $a = \sqrt{6}$ and $A = 120°$. Call the right side $b = 2$. The left angle is its opposite, so call this B. Use the formula $\frac{\sin A}{a} = \frac{\sin B}{b}$.

7. Answer: $\sqrt{6}$

Hints: Note that $\sqrt{2}$ is opposite to 30°. Call these $a = \sqrt{2}$ and $A = 30°$. Call the other angle $B = 120°$. The bottom side is its opposite, so call this b. Use the formula $\frac{\sin A}{a} = \frac{\sin B}{b}$. Note that $\sqrt{2}\sqrt{3} = \sqrt{2(3)} = \sqrt{6}$.

8. Answer: 75° (if you got 45°, you may have found the wrong angle; see below)

Hints: Note that 3 is opposite to 60°. Call these $a = 3$ and $A = 60°$. Call the left side $b = \sqrt{6}$. The right angle is its opposite, so call this B. Use the formula $\frac{\sin A}{a} = \frac{\sin B}{b}$ to find B (which is **not** the final answer). You should get $B = 45°$. Now find the third angle, C, knowing that the sum of the interior angles of any triangle is 180°.

9. Answer: 30° (if you got 120°, you may have found the wrong angle; see below)

Hints: Note that 1 is opposite to 30°. Call these $a = 1$ and $A = 30°$. Call the top side $b = \sqrt{3}$. The bottom angle is its opposite, so call this B. Use the formula $\frac{\sin A}{a} = \frac{\sin B}{b}$ to find B (which is **not** the final answer). You should get $B = 120°$. (Since the problem states that this triangle is obtuse, 60° would not work because that would result in a right triangle.) Now find the third angle, C, knowing that the sum of the interior angles of any triangle is 180°.

10. Answer: 30° or 90° (if you got 60° or 120°, you may have found the wrong angle)

Hints: Note that 1 is opposite to 30°. Call these $a = 1$ and $A = 30°$. Call the right side $b = \sqrt{3}$. The left angle is its opposite, so call this B. Use the formula $\frac{\sin A}{a} = \frac{\sin B}{b}$ to find B (which is **not** the final answer). You should get $B = 60°$ or 120° as possible answers. (In contrast to Problem 9, the instructions to Problem 10 do not specify the nature of any of the angles. Remember, it is not drawn to scale.) Now find the third angle, C, knowing that the sum of the interior angles of any triangle is 180°. You will get two possible answers, corresponding to the two possibilities for B. In one case, the triangle is right; in the other case, it is obtuse. (The left angle, B, may not "look" obtuse, but since the diagram is not drawn to scale, it could be.) Either way, the answer we are looking for is the bottom angle, C.

11. Answer: 105° (if you got 30°, you may have found the wrong angle; see below)

Hints: Note that $\sqrt{6}$ is opposite to 45°. Call these $a = \sqrt{6}$ and $A = 45°$. Call the right side $b = \sqrt{3}$. The left angle is its opposite, so call this B. Use the formula $\frac{\sin A}{a} = \frac{\sin B}{b}$ to find B (which is **not** the final answer). You should get $B = 30°$. Now find the third angle, C, knowing that the sum of the interior angles of any triangle is 180°.

12. Answer: $2\sqrt{2}$

Hints: Note that 2 is opposite to $30°$. Call these $a = 2$ and $A = 30°$. Call the other angle $B = 105°$. We need to find the third angle, C, because the top side is opposite to the bottom angle. Find C knowing that the sum of the interior angles of any triangle is $180°$. You should get $45°$. The top side is its opposite, so call this c. Use the formula $\frac{\sin A}{a} = \frac{\sin C}{c}$.

Chapter 11 Law of Cosines

1. Answer: $c^2 = a^2 + b^2 - 2ab \cos C$

Hints: Draw the height of the triangle, as shown below. The height divides the triangle into two small right triangles. Apply the Pythagorean theorem to each of these small right triangles. You should get $e^2 + h^2 = c^2$ and $d^2 + h^2 = b^2$. Eliminate h from these equations. (One way is to subtract the equations.) You should get $e^2 - d^2 = c^2 - b^2$. In the right triangle on the right, write down an equation for the cosine of angle C. You should get $d = b \cos C$. Note that $d + e = a$, such that $e = a - b \cos C$. Plug these expressions for d and e into $e^2 - d^2 = c^2 - b^2$. Recall from algebra that $(d + e)^2 = d^2 + 2de + e^2$. Simplify your answer.

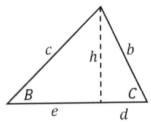

2. Answer: $a^2 + b^2 = c^2$

Hints: Set $C = 90°$ in $c^2 = a^2 + b^2 - 2ab \cos C$. Recall that $\cos 90° = 0$.

3. Answer: $135°$

Hints: Let $a = \sqrt{2}$, $b = 2$, and $c = \sqrt{10}$. Since we want the angle opposite to c, use the formula $c^2 = a^2 + b^2 - 2ab \cos C$. Plug in numbers and isolate the cosine. You should get $-\frac{1}{\sqrt{2}} = \cos C$. Take the inverse cosine of both sides. Note that cosine is negative in Quadrant II (and Quadrant III is clearly not viable for the interior angle of a triangle, since the three angles must add up to $180°$).

4. Answer: $\sqrt{3}$

Hints: Since the given angle is not opposite to either of the given sides, we must use three different letters: $a = \sqrt{3}$, $b = 3$, and $C = 30°$. Use the formula $c^2 = a^2 + b^2 - 2ab\cos C$. Plug in numbers. You should get $c^2 = 3$. Square root both sides. (Take the positive root since the length of a side cannot be negative.)

5. Answer: 13

Hints: Since the given angle is not opposite to either of the given sides, we must use three different letters: $a = 7$, $b = 8$, and $C = 120°$. Use the formula $c^2 = a^2 + b^2 - 2ab\cos C$. Plug in numbers. You should get $c^2 = 169$. Square root both sides.

6. Answer: $45°$

Hints: Let $a = 3$, $b = 2\sqrt{2}$, and $c = \sqrt{5}$. Since we want the angle opposite to c, use the formula $c^2 = a^2 + b^2 - 2ab\cos C$. Plug in numbers and isolate the cosine. You should get $\frac{1}{\sqrt{2}} = \cos C$. Take the inverse cosine of both sides.

7. Answer: $\sqrt{6}$

Hints: Since the given angle is not opposite to either of the given sides, we must use three different letters: $a = 2\sqrt{3}$, $b = \sqrt{6}$, and $C = 45°$. Use the formula $c^2 = a^2 + b^2 - 2ab\cos C$. Plug in numbers. You should get $c^2 = 6$. Square root both sides.

8. Answer: $150°$

Hints: Let $a = 2$, $b = 2\sqrt{3}$, and $c = 2\sqrt{7}$. Since we want the angle opposite to c, use the formula $c^2 = a^2 + b^2 - 2ab\cos C$. Plug in numbers and isolate the cosine. You should get $-\frac{\sqrt{3}}{2} = \cos C$. Take the inverse cosine of both sides. Note that cosine is negative in Quadrant II (and Quadrant III is clearly not viable for the interior angle of a triangle, since the three angles must add up to $180°$).

9. Answer: $3\sqrt{7}$

Hints: Since the given angle is not opposite to either of the given sides, we must use three different letters: $a = 6$, $b = 9$, and $C = 60°$. Use the formula $c^2 = a^2 + b^2 - 2ab\cos C$. Plug in numbers. You should get $c^2 = 63$. Square root both sides. Note that $\sqrt{63} = \sqrt{9(7)} = \sqrt{9}\sqrt{7} = 3\sqrt{7}$.

10. Answer: $30°$

Hints: Let $a = \sqrt{2}$, $b = \sqrt{6}$, and $c = \sqrt{2}$. Since we want the angle opposite to c, use the formula $c^2 = a^2 + b^2 - 2ab\cos C$. Plug in numbers and isolate the cosine. You should get $\frac{\sqrt{3}}{2} = \cos C$. Take the inverse cosine of both sides.

11. Answer: 90°

Hints: Let $a = \sqrt{2}$, $b = \sqrt{6}$, and $c = 2\sqrt{2}$. Since we want the angle opposite to c, use the formula $c^2 = a^2 + b^2 - 2ab\cos C$. Plug in numbers and isolate the cosine. You should get $0 = \cos C$. Take the inverse cosine of both sides.

12. Answer: $\sqrt{35}$

Hints: Since the given angle is not opposite to either of the given sides, we must use three different letters: $a = \sqrt{5}$, $b = \sqrt{15}$, and $C = 150°$. Use the formula $c^2 = a^2 + b^2 - 2ab\cos C$. Plug in numbers. You should get $c^2 = 35$. Square root both sides.

Chapter 12 Inverse Function Identities

1. Answers: $\sin(\sin^{-1} x) = x$, $\cos(\sin^{-1} x) = \sqrt{1 - x^2}$, $\tan(\sin^{-1} x) = \frac{x}{\sqrt{1-x^2}}$,

$\cot(\sin^{-1} x) = \frac{\sqrt{1-x^2}}{x}$, $\sec(\sin^{-1} x) = \frac{1}{\sqrt{1-x^2}}$, and $\csc(\sin^{-1} x) = \frac{1}{x}$

Hints: Sine is opposite over hypotenuse. Draw a right triangle where the opposite of θ is x and the hypotenuse is 1, like the diagram below. This way, $\sin\theta = \frac{x}{1} = x$ and $\theta = \sin^{-1} x$. Find $\sin\theta$, $\cos\theta$, $\tan\theta$, $\cot\theta$, $\sec\theta$, and $\csc\theta$ for the triangle below.

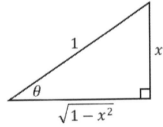

2. Answers: $\sin(\cos^{-1} x) = \sqrt{1 - x^2}$, $\cos(\cos^{-1} x) = x$, $\tan(\cos^{-1} x) = \frac{\sqrt{1-x^2}}{x}$,

$\cot(\cos^{-1} x) = \frac{x}{\sqrt{1-x^2}}$, $\sec(\cos^{-1} x) = \frac{1}{x}$, and $\csc(\cos^{-1} x) = \frac{1}{\sqrt{1-x^2}}$

Hints: Cosine is adjacent over hypotenuse. Draw a right triangle where the adjacent of θ is x and the hypotenuse is 1, like the diagram for Example 1. This way, $\cos\theta = \frac{x}{1} = x$ and $\theta = \cos^{-1} x$. Find $\sin\theta$, $\cos\theta$, $\tan\theta$, $\cot\theta$, $\sec\theta$, and $\csc\theta$ for the triangle.

3. Answers: $\sin(\tan^{-1} x) = \frac{x}{\sqrt{1+x^2}}$, $\cos(\tan^{-1} x) = \frac{1}{\sqrt{1+x^2}}$, $\tan(\tan^{-1} x) = x$,

$\cot(\tan^{-1} x) = \frac{1}{x}$, $\sec(\tan^{-1} x) = \sqrt{1 + x^2}$, and $\csc(\tan^{-1} x) = \frac{\sqrt{1+x^2}}{x}$

Hints: Tangent is opposite over adjacent. Draw a right triangle where the opposite of θ is x and the adjacent is 1, like the diagram below. This way, $\tan\theta = \frac{x}{1} = x$ and $\theta = \tan^{-1} x$. Find $\sin\theta$, $\cos\theta$, $\tan\theta$, $\cot\theta$, $\sec\theta$, and $\csc\theta$ for the triangle below.

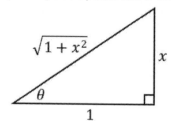

4. Answers: $\sin(\cot^{-1} x) = \frac{1}{\sqrt{1+x^2}}$, $\cos(\cot^{-1} x) = \frac{x}{\sqrt{1+x^2}}$, $\tan(\cot^{-1} x) = \frac{1}{x}$, $\cot(\cot^{-1} x) = x$, $\sec(\cot^{-1} x) = \frac{\sqrt{1+x^2}}{x}$, and $\csc(\cot^{-1} x) = \sqrt{1+x^2}$

Hints: Cotangent is adjacent over opposite. Draw a right triangle where the adjacent of θ is x and the opposite is 1, like the diagram below. This way, $\cot\theta = \frac{x}{1} = x$ and $\theta = \cot^{-1} x$. Find $\sin\theta$, $\cos\theta$, $\tan\theta$, $\cot\theta$, $\sec\theta$, and $\csc\theta$ for the triangle below.

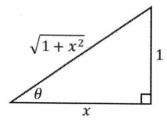

5. Answers: $\sin(\sec^{-1} x) = \frac{\sqrt{x^2-1}}{x}$, $\cos(\sec^{-1} x) = \frac{1}{x}$, $\tan(\sec^{-1} x) = \sqrt{x^2 - 1}$, $\cot(\sec^{-1} x) = \frac{1}{\sqrt{x^2-1}}$, $\sec(\sec^{-1} x) = x$, and $\csc(\sec^{-1} x) = \frac{x}{\sqrt{x^2-1}}$

Hints: Secant is hypotenuse over adjacent. Draw a right triangle where the hypotenuse is x and the adjacent of θ is 1, like the diagram below. This way, $\sec\theta = \frac{x}{1} = x$ and $\theta = \sec^{-1} x$. Find $\sin\theta$, $\cos\theta$, $\tan\theta$, $\cot\theta$, $\sec\theta$, and $\csc\theta$ for the triangle below.

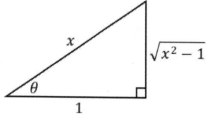

6. Answers: $\sin(\csc^{-1} x) = \frac{1}{x}$, $\cos(\csc^{-1} x) = \frac{\sqrt{x^2-1}}{x}$, $\tan(\csc^{-1} x) = \frac{1}{\sqrt{x^2-1}}$, $\cot(\csc^{-1} x) = \sqrt{x^2 - 1}$, $\sec(\csc^{-1} x) = \frac{x}{\sqrt{x^2-1}}$, and $\csc(\csc^{-1} x) = x$

Hints: Cosecant is hypotenuse over opposite. Draw a right triangle where the hypotenuse is x and the opposite of θ is 1, like the diagram below. This way, $\csc \theta = \frac{x}{1} = x$ and $\theta = \csc^{-1} x$. Find $\sin \theta$, $\cos \theta$, $\tan \theta$, $\cot \theta$, $\sec \theta$, and $\csc \theta$ for the triangle below.

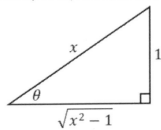

7. Answer: $\sec^{-1} x + \csc^{-1} x = \frac{\pi}{2}$

Hints: Draw a right triangle like the one we drew for Problem 5. Label the second acute angle φ. Review Example 2.

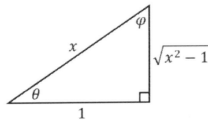

8. Answer: $\tan^{-1} x + \cot^{-1} x = \frac{\pi}{2}$

Hints: Draw a right triangle like the one we drew for Problem 3. Label the second acute angle φ. Review Example 2.

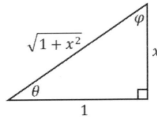

9. Answer: $\cos^{-1} x \pm \cos^{-1} y = \cos^{-1}\left(xy \mp \sqrt{(1 - x^2)(1 - y^2)}\right)$

Hints: Begin with the angle sum formula for cosine from Chapter 3 expressed in terms of θ and φ. Take the inverse cosine of both sides. Follow Example 3. Since cosine is adjacent over hypotenuse, draw a right triangle where the adjacent of θ is x and the hypotenuse is 1, and another right triangle where the adjacent of φ is y and the hypotenuse is 1. See the diagrams on the following page. The reason behind this is that $\cos \theta = \frac{x}{1} = x$ and $\cos \varphi = \frac{y}{1} = y$, such that $\theta = \cos^{-1} x$ and $\varphi = \cos^{-1} y$.

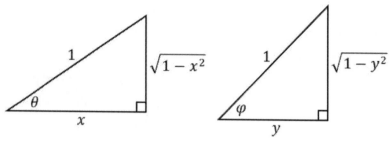

10. Answer: $\tan^{-1} x \pm \tan^{-1} y = \tan^{-1}\left(\frac{x\pm y}{1\mp xy}\right)$

Hints: Begin with the angle sum formula for tangent from Chapter 3 expressed in terms of θ and φ. Take the inverse tangent of both sides. Follow Example 3. Since tangent is opposite over adjacent, draw a right triangle where the opposite of θ is x and the adjacent is 1, and another right triangle where the opposite of φ is y and the adjacent is 1. See the diagrams below. The reason behind this is that $\tan\theta = \frac{x}{1} = x$ and $\tan\varphi = \frac{y}{1} = y$, such that $\theta = \tan^{-1} x$ and $\varphi = \tan^{-1} y$.

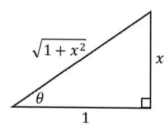
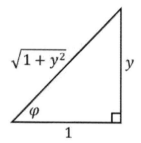

11. Answer: $\cot^{-1} x \pm \cot^{-1} y = \cot^{-1}\left(\frac{xy\mp 1}{y\pm x}\right)$

Hints: Begin with the angle sum formula for cotangent from Chapter 3 expressed in terms of θ and φ. Take the inverse cotangent of both sides. Follow Example 3. Since cotangent is adjacent over opposite, draw a right triangle where the adjacent of θ is x and the opposite is 1, and another right triangle where the adjacent of φ is y and the opposite is 1. See the diagrams below. The reason behind this is that $\cot\theta = \frac{x}{1} = x$ and $\cot\varphi = \frac{y}{1} = y$, such that $\theta = \cot^{-1} x$ and $\varphi = \cot^{-1} y$.

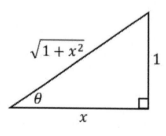
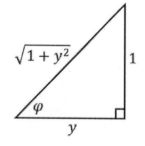

12. Answers: $\frac{\pi}{3}$ or $\frac{2\pi}{3}$ rad (corresponding to 60° or 120°)

Hint: Sine is positive in Quadrants I and II.

13. Answer: $0.8 = 4/5$ (using principal values; see page 63)

Note: We will restrict our answers to the principal values for identities of the form $\sin(\cos^{-1} x)$ where a trig function (not its inverse) is taken last, but not for identities of the form $\cos^{-1}(\cos x)$ where the inverse is taken last.

Hint: Use the corresponding inverse trig identity.

14. Answer: $\frac{1}{2\sqrt{2}} = \frac{1}{2\sqrt{2}}\frac{\sqrt{2}}{\sqrt{2}} = \frac{\sqrt{2}}{4}$ (using principal values)

Hints: Use the corresponding inverse trig identity. Note that $\sqrt{8} = \sqrt{4(2)} = \sqrt{4}\sqrt{2} = 2\sqrt{2}$. To divide two fractions, multiply by the reciprocal of the second fraction. To put the answer in standard form, rationalize the denominator.

15. Answers: $\frac{2\pi}{3}$ or $\frac{4\pi}{3}$ rad (corresponding to 120° or 240°)

Note that $-\frac{2\pi}{3}$ rad (corresponding to $-120°$) is equivalent to $\frac{4\pi}{3}$ rad (or 240°)

Hint: Cosine is negative in Quadrants II and III.

16. Answer: $\sqrt{5}$ (using principal values)

Hint: Use the corresponding inverse trig identity.

17. Answer: $\sqrt{10}$ (using principal values)

Hints: Use the corresponding inverse trig identity.

18. Answers: $\frac{5\pi}{6}$ or $\frac{11\pi}{6}$ rad (corresponding to 150° or 330°)

Note that $-\frac{\pi}{6}$ rad (corresponding to $-30°$) is equivalent to $\frac{11\pi}{6}$ rad (or 330°)

Hint: Tangent is negative in Quadrants II and IV.

19. Answer: $\frac{1}{1.5} = \frac{1}{3/2} = 1 \div \frac{3}{2} = 1 \times \frac{2}{3} = \frac{2}{3}$ (using principal values)

Hints: Use the corresponding inverse trig identity. Note that $1.5 = \frac{3}{2}$. To divide by a fraction, multiply by its reciprocal.

20. Answer: $\frac{\sqrt{7}}{3}$ (using principal values)

Hints: Use the corresponding inverse trig identity. Note that $\sqrt{\frac{7}{16}} = \frac{\sqrt{7}}{4}$. To divide two fractions, multiply by the reciprocal of the second fraction.

21. Answer: $\frac{5}{2\sqrt{6}} = \frac{5}{2\sqrt{6}}\frac{\sqrt{6}}{\sqrt{6}} = \frac{5\sqrt{6}}{12}$ (using principal values)

Hints: Use the corresponding inverse trig identity. Note that $\sqrt{24} = \sqrt{4(6)} = 2\sqrt{6}$. To put the answer in standard form, rationalize the denominator.

Chapter 13 Applications

1. Answers: $A = \sqrt{A_x^2 + A_y^2}$ and $\theta = \tan^{-1}\left(\frac{A_y}{A_x}\right)$

Hints: To isolate A, square the equations for A_x and A_y, and add them together. Apply the Pythagorean identity involving sine and cosine. To isolate θ, divide the equation for A_y by the equation for A_x. (Note that dividing equations is valid, provided that it does not result in division by zero. For example, if $a = b$ and $c = d$, it follows that $\frac{a}{c} = \frac{b}{d}$, provided that $c \neq 0$.)

2. Answers: $x = r \cos\theta$ and $y = r \sin\theta$

Hints: Solve for y in the second equation. You should get $y = x \tan\theta$. Substitute this into the first equation. Apply the Pythagorean identity involving tangent and secant. Square both sides. Isolate x. Substitute this into $y = x \tan\theta$.

3. Answers: $r = \sqrt{x^2 + y^2 + z^2}$, $\varphi = \cos^{-1}\left(\frac{z}{\sqrt{x^2+y^2+z^2}}\right)$, and $\theta = \tan^{-1}\left(\frac{y}{x}\right)$

Hints: This is similar to Problem 1, except for involving an extra variable. To isolate r, square the equations for x, y, and z, and add them together. Apply the Pythagorean identity involving sine and cosine twice (once for θ and once for φ). To isolate φ, solve for φ in the equation for z and substitute in the expression for r. To isolate θ, divide the equation for y by the equation for x.

4. Answers: $R = \frac{v_0^2}{g} \sin(2\theta_0)$ and $\theta_0 = \frac{\pi}{4}$ rad (corresponding to 45°)

Hints: Isolate t in the equation for x. You should get $t = \frac{x}{v_0 \cos\theta_0}$. Substitute this into the equation for y. Replace x with R. Multiply both sides of the equation by $\cos^2\theta_0$ and $2v_0^2$. Divide both sides of the equation by g. Apply the double angle formula for sine. For the second part of the problem, note that the sine function has a maximum of one when its argument equals $\frac{\pi}{2}$ rad (or 90°). Note that the argument is $2\theta_0$. Set $2\theta_0$ equal to $\frac{\pi}{2}$ rad. Divide both sides by 2 to solve for the maximum value of θ_0.

5. Answers: $T = m\sqrt{g^2 + \frac{v^4}{R^2}}$ and $\theta = \tan^{-1}\left(\frac{v^2}{Rg}\right)$

Hints: To isolate T, square both equations and add them together. Apply the Pythagorean identity involving sine and cosine. To isolate θ, divide the equation for $T\sin\theta$ by the equation for $T\cos\theta$.

6. Answer: $\cos\varphi = -\cos\theta$

Hints: Note that $\varphi + \theta = \pi$ rad (or 180°). Either use the sum of angles formula for cosine or use an identity from Chapter 9.

7. Answers: $\cos\alpha = \sin\theta$ and $\sin\alpha = \cos\theta$

Hints: Note that $\alpha + \theta = \frac{\pi}{2}$ rad (or 90°). Either use the sum of angles formula for sine and cosine or use identities from Chapter 9.

8. Answers: $y = D\cos(\omega t) + E\sin(\omega t)$, $A = \sqrt{D^2 + E^2}$, and $\varphi = \tan^{-1}\left(-\frac{E}{D}\right)$

Hints: Apply the sum of angles formula for cosine to get
$$y = A\cos(\omega t)\cos\varphi - A\sin(\omega t)\sin\varphi$$
To put this in the desired form, let
$$D = A\cos\varphi \quad , \quad E = -A\sin\varphi$$
Divide the second equation by the first equation to get
$$-\frac{E}{D} = \tan\varphi$$
Take the inverse tangent of both sides to get the equation for φ. Square the equations for D and E, and apply the Pythagorean identity involving sine and cosine to isolate A.

9. Answer: $\frac{\pi}{4} = \tan^{-1}\left(\frac{1}{2}\right) + \tan^{-1}\left(\frac{1}{3}\right)$

Hints: Use the $\tan^{-1}x + \tan^{-1}y$ identity from Chapter 12. You should get $\tan^{-1}\left(\frac{5/6}{5/6}\right)$ on the right, which simplifies to $\tan^{-1}1$, which equals $\frac{\pi}{4}$ rad (corresponding to 45°).

10. Answer: $y = 2A\cos(\pi f_b t)\cos(2\pi f_a t)$

Hints: This problem is much easier than it might look. Simply use a sum-to-product identity from Chapter 8, and make the substitutions $f_a = \frac{f_1 + f_2}{2}$ and $f_b = |f_1 - f_2|$.

WAS THIS BOOK HELPFUL?

A great deal of effort and thought was put into this book, such as:
- Providing several hints in the answer key to help walk students through the solutions to the problems.
- Careful selection of examples and problems for their instructional value.
- Coverage of a variety of essential trig identities.
- Emphasis on how to derive the trig identities, but also tabulating several trig identities in each chapter so that once the student has finished the book, it would still serve a useful purpose as a handbook.

If you appreciate the effort that went into making this book possible, there is a simple way that you could show it:

Please take a moment to post an honest review.

For example, you can review this book at Amazon.com or Goodreads.com.

Even a short review can be helpful and will be much appreciated. If you're not sure what to write, following are a few ideas, though it's best to describe what is important to you.
- How much did you learn from reading and using this workbook?
- Were the hints at the back of the book helpful?
- Were you able to understand the hints?
- Was it helpful to follow the examples while solving the problems?
- Would you recommend this book to others? If so, why?

Do you believe that you found a mistake? Please email the author, Chris McMullen, at greekphysics@yahoo.com to ask about it. One of two things will happen:
- You might discover that it wasn't a mistake after all and learn why.
- You might be right, in which case the author will be grateful and future readers will benefit from the correction. Everyone is human.

ABOUT THE AUTHOR

Dr. Chris McMullen has over 20 years of experience teaching university physics in California, Oklahoma, Pennsylvania, and Louisiana. Dr. McMullen is also an author of math and science workbooks. Whether in the classroom or as a writer, Dr. McMullen loves sharing knowledge and the art of motivating and engaging students.

The author earned his Ph.D. in phenomenological high-energy physics (particle physics) from Oklahoma State University in 2002. Originally from California, Chris McMullen earned his Master's degree from California State University, Northridge, where his thesis was in the field of electron spin resonance.

As a physics teacher, Dr. McMullen observed that many students lack fluency in fundamental math skills. In an effort to help students of all ages and levels master basic math skills, he published a series of math workbooks on arithmetic, fractions, long division, algebra, geometry, trigonometry, logarithms, and calculus entitled *Improve Your Math Fluency*. Dr. McMullen has also published a variety of science books, including astronomy, chemistry, and physics workbooks.

Author, Chris McMullen, Ph.D.

MATH

This series of math workbooks is geared toward practicing essential math skills:

- Prealgebra
- Algebra
- Geometry
- Trigonometry
- Logarithms and exponentials
- Calculus
- Fractions, decimals, and percentages
- Long division
- Multiplication and division
- Addition and subtraction
- Roman numerals
- The four-color theorem and basic graph theory

www.improveyourmathfluency.com

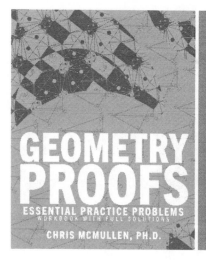

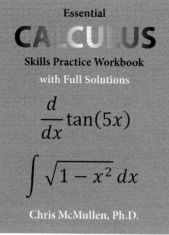

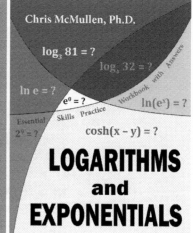

PUZZLES

The author of this book, Chris McMullen, enjoys solving puzzles. His favorite puzzle is Kakuro (kind of like a cross between crossword puzzles and Sudoku). He once taught a three-week summer course on puzzles. If you enjoy mathematical pattern puzzles, you might appreciate:

300+ Mathematical Pattern Puzzles

Number Pattern Recognition & Reasoning

- Pattern recognition
- Visual discrimination
- Analytical skills
- Logic and reasoning
- Analogies
- Mathematics

THE FOURTH DIMENSION

Are you curious about a possible fourth dimension of space?

- Explore the world of hypercubes and hyperspheres.
- Imagine living in a two-dimensional world.
- Try to understand the fourth dimension by analogy.
- Several illustrations help to try to visualize a fourth dimension of space.
- Investigate hypercube patterns.
- What would it be like to be a 4D being living in a 4D world?
- Learn about the physics of a possible four-dimensional universe.

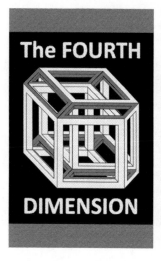
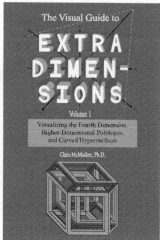
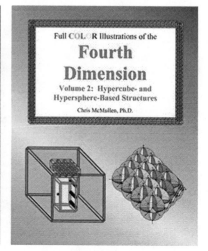

SCIENCE

Dr. McMullen has published a variety of **science** books, including:

- Basic astronomy concepts
- Basic chemistry concepts
- Balancing chemical reactions
- Calculus-based physics textbooks
- Calculus-based physics workbooks
- Calculus-based physics examples
- Trig-based physics workbooks
- Trig-based physics examples
- Creative physics problems
- Modern physics

www.monkeyphysicsblog.wordpress.com

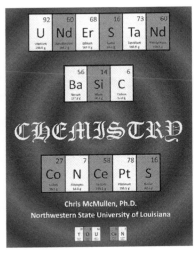

Made in United States
Troutdale, OR
10/20/2023

13881912R00071